"I would advise caution, Tara."

Damon's tone of voice was serious as he went on. "There is much passion in you that you're not yet aware of. A little warning might prevent you from being swept off your feet."

Furious at his words, Tara cried, "No man could do that to me—you talk nonsense!"

Too late she realized she had been foolish to express her feelings so candidly. His hold tightened and his lips crushed hers, encompassing her with fire and whirling her into a dizzying spiral of sensation.

Tara pulled away, but she felt a shock as Damon's dark eyes glittered derisively. "I'm merely trying to spare your pride, Miss Curtis," he said.

But Tara knew he was the kind of man who would spare nothing when it came to getting what he wanted—and he seemed to want her!

Autumn Song

by

MARGARET PARGETER

Harlequin Books

TORONTO·LONDON·NEW YORK·AMSTERDAM
SYDNEY·HAMBURG·PARIS·STOCKHOLM

Original hardcover edition published in 1979
by Mills & Boon Limited

ISBN 0-373-02350-2

Harlequin edition published August 1980

CHAPTER ONE

SHE stood on the waterfront at the seaport of Piraeus, a
slim slip of a girl, waiting for the ferry which would take
her on the last stage of her journey to the island of Polos.
Her tawny hair lifted imperceptibly in the light October
wind off the sea and her green eyes clouded as she raised
a hand to flick a heavy strand from her wide brow with
slender, pink-tipped fingers. Her face, for all her outward
composure, was young and pale, the soft, full curves of her
mouth betraying the emotions she tried to hide. It was
trembling slightly with some degree of uncertainty and
she tightened her lips so no one would notice. If anyone
was looking her way she wanted them to see confidence,
rather than nervousness.

The crowds were thin at this time of year, at this hour
of the day. People moved about her, their expressions
mixed. She saw the eager excitement of the tourist, the
preoccupation of the business man and sailor, the boredom
of the idle passers-by. Tara wondered what category she
came into. Panic rose as she decided she didn't fit in
here at all and, if she wasn't careful, the relative dignity
of her arrival could be lost in the haste of an ignominious
departure. Those who came here seeking information, however innocent, might not be treated kindly.

Such thoughts brought a return of the cowardly weakness which had attacked her so frequently over the past
few days. Her limbs shook and she stiffened them hastily.
Again she was fearful someone might spot her agitation
and be curious, but there were fortunately others who
attracted attention much more than herself. The man
striding her way, for instance. Tara allowed her flickering
glance to linger, aware of others doing the same. Those

who didn't recognise him obviously thought they should.
It wasn't just his tall, well-proportioned figure, although
this in itself was enough to make anyone look twice. He
had the kind of face seldom seen outside Greek mythology,
a kind of rugged beauty which caught the eye, which
might have been chiselled out of stone. No longer in his
first youth, he was undeniably handsome, with the unmistakable imprint of breeding, arrogance and pride. Tara's
breath unaccountably shuddered, coming to such a halt
as to make her next one almost painful. Greek, she decided,
right through to his very bones, in his blood, every ruthless, inescapable inch of him! Helplessly she bowed her
head as apprehension again washed over her and she hoped
fervently that all Greek men were not alike. That this tall
stranger didn't remotely resemble the one whose house
on Polos she had so foolishly agreed to watch.

She had expected such a superior being to walk straight
past and felt stunned with surprise when he stopped immediately beside her. As she sharply lifted her fair head
she felt his eyes flickering deliberately over her, calculating
interest in their dark depth.

While, at close quarters, the impression of ruthlessness
became a fact, she didn't think he was the kind of man
who picked girls up. A man like this wouldn't need to.
He would be amused at the very suggestion! For a peculiar moment, as they stood silently, her glance was no less
exploratory than his. He made an impact, but he also
frightened. His face was dark, his skin swarthy. There was
more than a hint of passion in his mouth, a trace of impatience in his piercing eyes. Tara wondered, with a
sudden quirk of very adult perception, if the two went
together. Shivering, she pushed the thought from her.

The man turned and Tara felt her breathing return
to normal, but only for a second. He had looked his fill,
half shaken his head and made to leave her, then swung
back frowning.

He asked shortly, his English almost without accent,

'Are you by any chance the young lady I am looking for, Miss Curtis, Miss Tara Curtis?'

'Yes,' her reply was brief. She could only stare in wordless astonishment. She could actually feel herself groping for words. Finding none, she nodded, as if seeking to confirm her assent. Why should this man be looking for her?

He frowned, as if no less surprised than herself but not choosing to disbelieve her. 'Indeed!' His gaze left her to consider disparagingly the two pieces of shabby luggage at her feet. He gave the distinct impression, as he bent to retrieve it, that he considered the suitcases like their owner. 'Is this all you have?' he asked.

'Yes.'

As if cynically amused by her apparently limited vocabulary, his well shaped mouth curled. 'Come, Miss Curtis, we will get you on board. Then you might find it possible to pull yourself together and find something more to say for yourself.'

On board! Muddled visions of the days when these seas were given over to robbers, cruel pirates of the Barbary coast, rose dramatically before Tara's tired eyes. Very quickly she came to life. Suddenly she was pulling at his powerful arms, attempting to stop him as he strode away from her, taking with him all her worldly possessions.

'You must wait!' she cried huskily, raising to him a face which was both bewildered and alarmed. 'Who are you? I don't even know you, although you clearly know me! But I'm not going anywhere with a stranger. I'm waiting for the ferry.'

'You are?' Impatient of her detaining hand, he stared down at it pointedly.

Flushing, she withdrew it, feeling as she did so a fiery tingle in her fingers, as if the circulation had received a sudden jolt. Nervously she clenched them behind her back as she lifted her tenderly cleft chin to stare up at him. 'Certainly !' she emphasised.

Her rising panic, which she tried to hide, seemed perversely to amuse him. 'The steamer has gone,' he said suavely. 'You ought to have hurried. It is October, Miss Curtis, and they don't run so frequently to the smaller islands. To many of the smaller islands they won't return, not until the spring flowers again carpet the land and the wind blows warm over the sea. To my island they might venture twice a month at the most, at any time of the year.'

'Your island?'

He smiled, his teeth gleaming white, which ought to have been reassuring but somehow was not. He had too much the look of the predator, despite his air of apparent civility.

'My island,' he repeated, his eyes appraising. 'The home of your good brother and his wife, Veronica. Does not the thought of it intrigue you?'

'You—you own it?'

Again his teeth glinted, as she flashed him a horrified glance. 'Do not look so put out, Miss Curtis. It happens to be true that I own over half of the actual land and have, shall we say, a great deal of interest in everything else.'

Tara's face went white. Her fingers clenched convulsively and she could have sworn the very ground heaved under her feet. 'Then you—you must be——?'

'Damon Voulgaris,' the slight bow from the waist was vaguely foreign but she suspected hid irony. 'No doubt your brother has mentioned me?'

No false modesty here! Assurance permeated every bit of him! 'Of course,' Tara's eyes darkened, 'but I didn't expect ...'

As her voice trailed off in confusion, he asked quietly, 'What didn't you expect, Miss Curtis?'

'I——' She drew a deep breath. She might as well be frank, although it wasn't easy. 'I certainly never imagined I'd be met by a man of your importance. Someone once mentioned that you're a millionaire.'

His voice was mocking. 'There are many millionaires in Greece, Miss Curtis. Do you imagine a man walks in a different light, a different world, because he has made money?'

'I should have thought so.' Helplessly her glance went over his broad shoulders, recognising the quality of the clothes he wore, which their casualness failed to disguise. The cut of his cotton pants, alone, was superb. She ought to have noticed, this and other things. The faultless, awesome power of the man, the way it appeared to radiate effortlessly from him!

'I'll admit, Miss Curtis, that money opens many doors which might otherwise be closed, but it doesn't buy everything. Otherwise I might go in for collecting wide-eyed little girls, if only because a Greek sets great store by innocence. Our gods always admired it, *thespinis*, but it is rare. Rarer still to find and keep for one's own.'

Tara flushed, hanging her head. He looked straight at her when he spoke and she couldn't pretend his words were not in some way connected with herself. The softness of the air, the magic of the approaching evening, perhaps lent to them a deeper meaning than was intended. She would be very naïve indeed to be taken in by the flattering tongue of this tall, handsome Greek, whose everyday conversation with women probably included more than a sprinkling of what she had just listened to.

When she raised her head again he was smiling, his expression amazingly kind. 'You are not aware, child, of having this aura of being beyond approach?'

The voice of her younger brother came back to her. 'No one would ever suspect you of anything devious, Tara, you have such a guileless face. It will help you as much as anything else to gain admittance to the house of the great Voulgaris.'

Tara turned this face, of which Jonathan so approved, unhappily towards the ships riding at anchor in the harbour. A weight of guilt bore down heavily. Doubts—the same doubts which had been plaguing her for days—accumulated, distressing her. It was becoming increasingly clear that she had been more than impulsively foolish in agreeing to do as Jonathan asked. Never had she remotely expected to have to take on a man like this. And while the invidious position she found herself in might provide a valid excuse for not travelling with him, her hands were tied as she could never explain. Some would consider the very gods which Damon Voulgaris had spoken of had dropped a bonus in her lap, because of this meeting, but she felt too apprehensive to appreciate it. If she had had any choice in the matter, she would have chosen to have met him another time, or not at all.

From the expression on his face it appeared his patience was running out, so she answered him hastily, a trifle dryly. 'I must ask you not to credit me with too many irreproachable qualities, Mr Voulgaris. I might find such a reputation difficult to live up to.'

'Well, there is very rarely the rose without a thorn,' he agreed whimsically. 'Perhaps it is your opinion of me, at the moment, which is the more important. Tell me, Miss Curtis, have you yet decided whether you will make the journey to Polos on my boat, or is there something else you wish to know before you can trust yourself to me?'

She tried to answer his faint smile. 'I'm sorry, Mr Voulgaris, if I seem too reluctant, but if you had a sister you wouldn't approve of her going off with a complete stranger, not without asking a few questions first.'

'If I had a sister she would not be standing here alone, Miss Curtis.'

'No—I see.'

'I doubt you do,' he sighed. 'It would take longer than a few minutes, I'm afraid, for you to understand why our Greek women don't have quite the same freedom as the *Anglika*. Nor do they run the same risks!'

Doubtfully, Tara shrank away from him slightly, finding in his words a kind of cloaked threat. In spite of his professed respect for her apparent innocence, there was something about him to make her pulse beat faster, to jangle warning bells in her head. Her face paled and the eyes she raised to his narrowed ones were still uncertain.

For another long moment he surveyed her, his sigh of intolerance actually reaching her ears. 'Come, Miss Curtis, now you know who I am there can be no further need for hesitation. Tomorrow you will be on Polos, safe with your admirable brother. Meanwhile you must have faith in me.'

'Tomorrow?' Her voice rose in despair, and some confusion. Panting a little, she stumbled alongside him as, apparently not willing to humour her any longer, he started off. She was unable to match his long strides but, as he was carrying her luggage, she felt unable to complain. 'Tomorrow,' she cried breathlessly. 'Why not until tomorrow, Mr Voulgaris?'

'Because of the distance?'

'Don't you usually fly?' She had thought most men as wealthy as Voulgaris used planes.

'I'm taking my yacht.'

'Oh, I see.'

'Take care you don't see too much with those beautiful green eyes of yours, Miss Curtis. With their help, plus a little imagination, you appear to see the worst of everything.'

As she clambered behind him, on board an elegant white boat, Tara shivered. Was this a warning? Beneath the surface, under all that dark, disturbing charm, she sensed that this man could be dangerous, but never in all her twenty-two years had she met anyone like him. How crazy had Jonathan been in deciding she could get past him! 'Try and discover if Greg Golden, the pop star, really is hiding on the island,' he'd said. 'He's a friend of Damon Voulgaris, the Greek millionaire, and would be staying at his villa. Voulgaris, though, is unlikely to be there.'

But he was there, even before she'd set foot on the island, issuing orders—or warnings, she wasn't quite sure which. She was only aware of the ominous ring to his voice, the enigmatic gleam in his eye.

The yacht was tied up at the quay; obviously Damon Voulgaris would have his own private moorings. To Tara's dazed eyes it looked quite splendid, a shining example of what a well cared for boat should be. Whichever way she looked there was the gleam of white paintwork and brass, burnished wood. She had hoped, vaguely, they might be sailing in one of the Greek caiques she had read so much about. She believed Tim, the brother she was visiting, helped to build them. Or had built them? She wasn't quite sure if this was what he was still doing. Lately they had very seldom heard from him and he had stopped mentioning the island. Why was this? Tara pondered. This was one of the reasons why their parents had been so keen for Tara to come out here. They had sensed that all was not well and were worried. Perhaps it was merely because Tim had extra work to do in the taverna which he and his wife ran between them.

At the top of the gangway she wasn't allowed a further look around. Quickly, Damon Voulgaris took her down a flight of steps, speaking curtly in Greek to a man who hurried forward to meet them. The steward picked up her suitcase while Damon Voulgaris turned to her.

'Georgios will take you along to your cabin, Miss Curtis. We don't dine until eight, so you should have enough time. I have further business to attend to.'

As he paused, his eyes for some reason seeming reluctant to leave her, her mind seized on what he had just said. For the space of seconds she saw the opportunity to elude him, but he smashed her hopes before they were scarcely born.

Nearer he came, his eyes still fixed on her face. 'Doesn't escape seem too dramatic a thought to have in mind, Miss Curtis?' His hand shot out and this time it was her arm that was gripped and held tightly. 'I can assure you you will travel much more comfortably with me than with many another. You will be safer, too, for there are those who haven't an over-abundance of respect for the young girl who travels alone. Content yourself, Miss Curtis, that when I communicate with your brother he will be happy to know you are being well taken care of. It was he who asked me to look out for you.'

This, giving the impression that Tim and this man were friendly, she found disquieting, and tried not to think of the implications. 'Yes,' she consented uneasily, and was relieved that he seemed satisfied and turned away.

Her eyes widened with bemused hostility as she watched his long powerful legs disappearing back up the short flight of steps. No doubt he knew exactly the kind of effect he had on a woman when he chose to exert himself, but she had no intention of succumbing to his charm. The strange feelings which went through her when he looked at her she didn't understand and pushed them aside. Once he learnt how she had promised to help Jonathan he might shortly be throwing her off his precious island. Very soon he might come to regret deeply ever bringing her there!

The suite she was shown to was the last word in luxury. Tara, who had never been on a large yacht before, was bemused by it. Everything spoke of money, tastefully spent but money all the same. Blinking, rather nervously, she stared around, not sure what to make of it. The thick white carpet alone must have cost more than she was used to spending in a year, and the fitments, in a gleaming, satiny wood, were beautiful. It was more like a bedroom in a grand house than a cabin. The uneasy feeling in her stomach grew worse as she sank down on the edge of a superbly padded chair, unconsciously rubbing the arm which Voulgaris's hand had bruised.

Her position was hateful. It was growing more so by the minute, so far as she could see, but what could she do about it? On the face of things she was just a young English girl going to spend a few weeks with her brother and his wife. Unfortunately, because of the brother who lived in England, the real picture was somewhat different. Why, she wondered, head in hands, had she ever listened to Jonathan? Was it because she was a girl and so much younger than her two brothers that she always seemed to be at everyone's beck and call?

When Tara had left school at eighteen, her father had become ill and her mother had subsequently gone out to work. It had seemed more sensible that Tara should stay at home and look after him while her fully trained mother earned enough to keep the house going. Fortunately, perhaps, Tara's brothers had both left home years before this so had not had to be provided for. Tim, the elder one, whom she was on her way to visit, had married and, with his wife, kept a taverna on a Greek island. Jonathan, two years younger than Tim, worked on a large provincial newspaper, a hundred miles south of the small north-country town where they had all been born. It was on the strength of Jonathan's apparently growing reputation as a reporter that Tara had been given some part-time work on their local newspaper. She had covered the children's pony sports, the junior tennis tournament, the noisy disco which the older staff shunned. Tara had been glad of the opportunity, not because of any great enthusiasm for the job, but it had taken her away from the house for a few hours each week and earned her a little money.

Then her father had recovered and her mother went back to doing only locum work for the panel of doctors. Tara was free at last to start thinking of a career. At almost twenty-two it was a bit late but not impossible, but a letter a week ago from Tim, on Polos, had resulted in this having to be shelved again. H' wife, Veronica, wanted a little help in the taverna. It would only be for a few weeks, with the last of the summer tourists. He had had to spend so much time assisting her, his boat building business was slipping.

Apart from this he would appreciate seeing some of his family.

So, unable to refuse, as she was the only one willing and entirely free, Tara had agreed to go. It was a break she had looked forward to, even with excitement, in spite of knowing that Veronica would probably expect her to work hard. Tara might still have been keen about it if it hadn't been for Jonathan's lightning visit when he had learnt where she was off to.

Jonathan's wife was expecting her first baby and it was imperative that he got promotion, so they might move into better accommodation. He was in line for promotion, he only needed a lucky break to tip the scales in his favour. This lucky break might, he had said, be just within his grasp if Tara would agree to help.

Apparently Greg Golden, the famous pop star, had disappeared. Not even his fiancée seemed to know where he was, but Jonathan had been tipped off that he might be, of all places, on Polos, hiding in the villa of the Greek millionaire Damon Voulgaris.

'Where Golden is concerned,' Jonathan had declared, 'it would be a scoop with even the biggest daily, especially as it's rumoured he could be having personal problems, maybe over his engagement. You wouldn't know,' Jonathan had explained, seeing Tara's puzzled glance, 'that Golden's fiancée is Lord Felton's daughter, a right little bitch, if ever there was one! It's common knowledge that she openly insulted the old man, my editor, and if this news is true and I uncover it, I'm sure I'll never look back.'

'How did Lord Felton's daughter insult your editor?' Tara had asked, playing for time, rather than because she was over-curious. She hadn't been quite sure what Jonathan was about to ask, but she had had the horrid feeling she wasn't going to like it.

'It was when the engagement was announced. Lord Felton lives down our way, you see, and as the old man knows him well, he was counting on getting the inside story. Miss Felton, however, was openly insulting and simply showed him the door. He's been livid ever since.'

'But what on earth can I do?' Tara had murmured anxiously. 'I don't know what influence this Greek millionaire has, but if I start poking my nose in his business, or that of his guests, couldn't it have an adverse effect on Tim? After all, he has to live there!'

'Tim won't know. No one need know—that you're involved, that is. The information I'm after won't be that difficult to come by. All I'm asking you to do is to confirm that Golden is there. If I went myself that might really put Tim in a spot as Golden can spot a reporter like me a mile off. They acquire a kind of built-in radar regarding newspaper men and I'd only be thrown out.'

'Thrown out?'

'Yes, well,' Jonathan's shrug had been wonderfully careless, 'Voulgaris has a lot of influence on the island and things are often not quite so civilised over there, but I happen to know he's in Australia at the moment, so you shouldn't have him to contend with. In any case Voulgaris would never suspect you.'

All the time she bathed and dressed, Tara kept telling herself she wasn't in any way compelled to do as Jonathan asked, that there was no reason why the thought of frail little Julia having her first baby in an attic room should haunt her. Julia could have come up North and let Mum look after her. The trouble was Jonathan wouldn't let her out of his sight, not even after three years of marriage. It didn't seem to make sense! As for Voulgaris being in Australia, that must be the laugh of the century, because he was here, and she had no particular fancy to take him on in anything! The very thought of snooping around his property to see who might be sunning themselves on his terraces was enough to make her blood run cold—when she considered the risk. Not for one moment did it cross her mind that, with her looks, there might be other ways of getting what she wanted.

Moodily she wandered to the porthole, staring out over the dark, silky waters of the Aegean. They were still in port as the boat was exactly where it had been when she had come on board. Her mind full of regret, she stared blindly, unaware of the passing time. How she wished she had never done any work for the local paper. Jonathan appeared to imagine she had all the experience of a full-time journalist and should know exactly how to go about this mission he had more or less forced on her.

'Use your instinct and common sense, infant,' he'd said impatiently. Right now Tara felt she had neither!

There was a knock on the door, startling her, but when she went it was only Georgios, informing her that dinner was ready. Too late Tara wished she had pretended a headache and stayed in her cabin. Even if he was rich and could afford it, under the circumstances, she would feel like a thief, taking Damon Vougaris's food.

The dress she wore was cotton, mid-calf and informal, the low, rounded neckline showing her firm young figure to advantage but otherwise making no noticeable contribution towards the glamour of the occasion. She had brought along a long skirt but, in her position, it would surely be presumptuous to dress up. Quite possibly Damon Voulgaris only intended giving her a snack in the galley. Her longish fair hair she brushed carelessly around her small, graceful head and apart from a pink lipstick, applied lightly, used no make-up. Without bothering to take so much as a final glance in the huge mirror, Tara left her cabin.

Contrary to her former expectations, Damon Voulgaris awaited her in the main salon, an apartment as luxurious as the one she had just vacated. A hint of humour struck her, momentarily dismissing her growing apprehension. He was impeccably dressed in a white jacket and tie and she found herself wondering wryly if he had ever sat down to dinner with a girl as economically gowned as herself.

As he strolled forward, his eyes narrowly considered

the flicker of derision in hers. 'You are amused, Miss Curtis?'

'No—not really,' she replied quickly, her eyes cautious on the hard line of his mouth. 'That is, if I was, it could only be at myself.'

'Then may I share this joke?' He placed a glass of sherry in her hands, his eyes no less probing.

Tara stared into the wine-red depth of her glass uneasily. How to confess that if she had ever dreamed of coming to the island, during the past years, it had been in a much more romantic style than this? In her dreams she had seen herself gliding over the blue Aegean, as Ulysses might have done, in an open caique, the soft evening wind in its sails, the whisper of it in her ears. This, of course, she had known to be impossible, even before she had stepped from the plane which had brought her to Athens. More prosaically she had been prepared to face the prospect of a crowded ferry, too afraid of being dropped off on the wrong island to remember, or regret, even a half of the foolish things she had dreamt of. Never had she envisioned reaching Polos on the beautiful yacht of the very man she was being practically forced to spy on!

Aware that Damon Voulgaris waited, she replied hastily, 'I've led a very quiet life, Mr Voulgaris. Now it appears, everything happens.'

'Quiet?'

'Well, you know. Uneventful ...'

'Uneventful?' He pounced on the word with a kind of deadly accuracy, his eyes resting with ruthless interest on the full curves which her sloppy shirt had disguised. 'What do you mean by that exactly, Miss Curtis?'

'Why, not a great deal.' A strange warmth invading her body, she stared at him. 'I suppose, that I haven't travelled a lot.'

His smile was nothing more than a cynical twist of the lips. 'Your life need not have proved uneventful simply because you haven't visited many places.'

He stepped nearer, his tall, lithe body within touching distance, his eyes not allowing hers to turn aside. It was like being trapped in a whirlpool of curious darkness. She had the odd sensation of floating, of being completely at the mercy of something which threatened her.

She swallowed, wondering why the effort should be so painful, wishing she had even a modicum of sophistication to draw on. 'You—you're referring to the way I've lived, Mr Voulgaris?' she stammered.

'Obviously,' he assented dryly. 'You have a curiously untouched look about you which is rarely encountered. Are you all you appear to be, Miss Curtis, or is this air about you, which might intrigue a man, deceptive?'

An Englishman, Tara was sure, would never have asked such a pertinent question, on such a short acquaintance. Or, if he had, he wouldn't have put it in quite the same way. This man, this tall Greek, could with a word or look convey an impression of intimacy which she had never before experienced. Flushing, she drew herself a little away, as if an extra inch might protect her from his disturbing masculinity. 'That's my own business, surely? I've never had much time or inclination to study my appearance, or to worry as to what construction someone like yourself might put on it.'

He laughed, as though he mocked her stilted little sentences. 'It proves your inexperience, does it not, that you grow tense and wary whenever a man comes near you, or wishes to know about you. But do not be so agitated,' he smiled. 'Curiously enough, innocence can often protect much better than bravado. As for my questions, which you secretly consider presumptuous, another girl might be flattered.'

'Naturally, Mr Voulgaris, with your wealth most women would be flattered to have you around, no matter what you asked.'

His eyes narrowed, glinting with the sharp intelligence which already had her worried. 'You keep referring to my wealth, Miss Curtis?'

'I——Oh, yes. Of course,' she stammered, casting around in her mind despairingly. 'My brother Tim ...'

'I shouldn't have thought Tim would have mentioned it. His wife, perhaps ...'

'Veronica doesn't write. No, it must have been Tim. Or perhaps it's this yacht. It's not exactly a—er—poor man's boat, is it?' she finished, in dry desperation.

At the steward's discreet signal they moved into a smart dining salon. As she sat down, Voulgaris said coolly, 'Your tone suggests you don't approve of men with money.'

'I'm afraid I haven't known many, not personally.'

'Yet your brother's marriage, I believe, might be vastly improved by a little more of it.'

Startled, Tara grasped the slender stem of the glass he had just filled with the palest of wines. Bubbles rose from its golden transparency as it tilted slightly in her hand. 'You—you mean Tim, of course?'

'Who else?' His eyes were on the nervous tremor of her hand. 'You do have another brother, though.'

'Yes,' she replied quickly, refusing even to give his name. Tim might not have mentioned it, seeing how these last few years, he had barely kept in touch. Seeking to divert Damon Voulgaris's attention from Jonathan, she plunged haphazardly into a topic she had had no intention of discussing even briefly. 'It must be Tim's own fault that he's not financially secure. He failed his medical exams and quarrelled with his father, but Daddy has been ill recently and I think it's taught him to be more tolerant. He even talks of coming to see Tim himself next year.'

'I see. This is news.' There was a pregnant pause while Damon Voulgaris's dark eyes flicked her hot face with the cool glitter of diamonds. 'Your brother talks to me, Miss Curtis, but he doesn't tell me everything.'

Perhaps because he said so little, she found herself

rushing on, 'Tim left medical school against his father's wishes and married Veronica. Actually,' Tara confessed, feeling terribly ashamed, 'none of us has ever met her. Daddy wanted him to stay on, you see, and re-sit his exams, but Tim wouldn't. Anyway, he had some money left him and came out here. For several years we never heard from him. Now he occasionally sends Mum a letter and she writes back.'

'Didn't you ever think of putting pen to paper yourself? I know he has felt cut off from his family.'

She didn't imagine the faint note of criticism, it was there! Lifting her eyes from her sparkling glass she sought to defend herself against his ironic attack, 'I was only fifteen when all this happened, almost seven years ago. I do realise, of course, that in Greece family ties are often much closer than those of some other countries, which might make it difficult for you to understand.'

'So,' his dark brows lifted slightly at her condescension, 'you have reached the great age of twenty-two and still feel justified in criticising your brother. From what I've heard you haven't achieved all that much yourself, Tara Curtis.'

Tara looked up from her fish, grilled on charcoal and served with herbs and oil and lemon sauce. It was delicious and, after the first wonderful mouthful, she had decided to satisfy a very youthful hunger. She had hoped, seeing how delicious the meal was, he might consider they had talked enough about a family he scarcely knew. Now, alarmingly, he was hinting that he knew more than she supposed.

Resentment showed on her face in spite of her faint effort to restrain it, and her reply was out before she could fully control her voice, either. 'Seeing how you already know so much about me, Mr Voulgaris, I think you had a nerve to resent my knowing something about you—— That you're very rich.'

His teeth glinted, devilishly white against his dark tan, as he watched her pink cheeks. 'Eat your fish, Tara. So far I have received few answers to my polite queries. True, you have parted with a little information but only, I believe, reluctantly, and, for some reason not immediately apparent, to divert me.'

'And you're not used to—to people being unco-operative?'

'Let me just say that few people, least of all women, would care to offend me, Tara.'

The arrogance of the man! Quickly Tara lowered her thick, curling lashes, cloaking her anger. She remembered Tim once writing, 'Every now and again you come across a Greek who defies description.' He hadn't gone on to explain what he'd meant, but Tara thought she knew! At least she did now. First Damon Voulgaris called her '*thespinis*', which she fancied meant girl. Now it was Tara, without so much as asking if she minded. The way he pronounced her name set her curiously on edge. It was almost as if he were testing the flavour of it, and she felt disturbed, uncertain, out of her depth. Yet wouldn't she be foolish to antagonise him when, without even asking, he might unwittingly divulge the information which Jonathan was after? Once it was in her possession, all she would have to do was relay it, then she could forget it and concentrate on helping Veronica and Tim.

With this firmly in mind, she said evenly, 'I certainly don't wish to offend you, Mr Voulgaris, especially for Tim's sake. After all, I shall be here only for a short time while he has to live on your island.'

'Tim doesn't have to do anything, Miss Curtis. I have no absolute authority over him. He is free to come and go as he pleases.' Voulgaris paused, staring at her narrowly. 'But I'm not sure if I'll allow you the same privileges. It rather depends on several things which I'm not at this moment prepared to discuss.'

CHAPTER TWO

INSTINCTIVELY Tara stiffened, alarm shooting through her as, involuntarily, she stared at Damon Voulgaris's enigmatical dark face. How silky his voice yet how harsh his expression! One seemed strangely at variance with the other, but she wasn't sure which she disliked most. She was conscious of her heartbeats, of his eyes, granite-hard, as he returned her long stare, and she had the most peculiar feeling that he was wishing he had never met her.

Which all appeared to point at suspicion, of one kind or another. Desperately she tried to keep her growing panic under control, hating Jonathan afresh for what he was doing to her. If Damon Voulgaris was hiding Greg Golden, wouldn't he naturally be wary of anyone who came to the island? She couldn't hope to escape his grim surveillance, but he was obviously too cautious to accuse her outright regarding her motives, not without the right kind of evidence. Fate having conveniently thrown her into his hands, he had apparently decided a few cloaked threats wouldn't come amiss. Hadn't he already warned her about seeing too much?

With a carelessness she was far from feeling, Tara shrugged, forcing a light smile. 'You talk in riddles, Mr Voulgaris. As we're strangers I'm sure we can't have anything of importance to discuss. I'm equally sure that, when the time comes for me to leave your island, which I haven't yet set foot on, you'll never dream of doing anything to stop me.'

His slight smile of appreciation taunted. 'You have a rare turn of speech, Miss Curtis. It's almost as if you were used to putting your thoughts down on paper.'

Faint traces of guilt touched her cheeks with colour and

23

she clenched her fists under the table in angry frustration. Anger at Jonathan, irritation with herself, a furious resentment at the man who continued to goad her. His taunting wasn't just accidental, she could see, and she felt she could very easily hate him for it. Emotion, inexplicably fierce, moved through her, the temptation to strike his mocking face with her bare hand almost irresistible. Only the thought of actually touching his hard, tanned cheek gave her the strength to restrain herself. Physical contact of any kind with Damon Voulgaris was something she chose not to think about.

Pushing her plate aside, she said tersely, 'You seem to enjoy insulting me, Mr Voulgaris, if not in actual words then by implication, and I'm scarcely in a position to retaliate.'

She held her breath as he was clearly about to ask what methods of retaliation she would use if she were in a more favourable position, then almost sighed with trembling relief as he obviously changed his mind.

Relenting, his glance travelled to her half empty plate. 'You must be very hungry. Don't let me spoil your appetite with my cynicism, Miss Curtis, otherwise my chef might feel insulted too.'

It was humiliating to suspect he would consider the feelings of his cook more important than those of a girl he was merely obliging with a lift, but she thought it wiser not to argue. The meal was delicious, and he was right, she was hungry. Though conscious of his continuing regard, Tara did it full justice. She even drank the wine he poured with a rare recklessness quite foreign to her nature, in an effort to eradicate the more disturbing details of her own treachery. In a certain measure she succeeded. Replete, she allowed herself to be led back to the main salon and plied with fragrant Turkish coffee.

Damon Vougaris had a strong mouth and it tilted with amusement as he refilled her cup. 'I'm happy to see you have enjoyed your meal, Miss Curtis.'

Embarrassed, she set down her cup quickly. She noticed he didn't hope she had, as was more usual. Betraying colour tinted her smooth cheeks again. She must have made a pig of herself, but it was unkind of him to hint. It came to her suddenly that Damon Voulgaris would not naturally be particularly kind to women, for all the superior tone of his previous declaration that Greek women were to be revered. He had been around, he was much travelled. She didn't know if he was wholly Greek, but with his looks and money he could probably do and say what he liked and get away with it. In her position, she realised, many other women would consider themselves very fortunate and would be making the most of the opportunity to flirt with him. Unfortunately, Tara thought wryly, she wouldn't know where to start. With a man like this, who gave the impression of being both sophisticated and ruthless, she'd be quite out of her depth.

'Don't look so confused,' he drawled, with a teasing gentleness which confounded her silent theories and had the profound effect of making her feel slightly ashamed. He smiled. 'I don't suppose you've eaten much all day, but believe me, it makes a delightful change to dine with a woman who obviously appreciates what one provides.'

Faintly Tara tried to smile.

'You are still doubtful?' He came down beside her on the leather seat, turning to look at her. 'How old are you, Tara?'

She had a certainty he knew but obliged. 'Twenty-two.'

'So old?' His dark brows rose. 'You look about seventeen. You did tell me before, but I wanted to make sure. You look such an infant with your porcelain skin and features which few men might long resist.'

She sensed, in a way which reminded her too sharply that she was perhaps more feminine than she supposed, that he had deliberately condensed the latter half of his sentence for fear of frightening her. There had been a definite urge in him to describe her other assets in more detail. Again she tried to smile lightly. 'That, at any rate, is a typically male reply. Why do men like to insist that every woman looks about seventeen? You probably wish we could stay that age for ever.'

His mouth quirked, matching the gleam in his eyes. 'Then I must be the exception. At thirty-six I've long outgrown the desire to be involved with teenagers. I prefer the more sophisticated woman who knows what she is doing or the rather more mature girl who is willing to learn.'

Almost visibly Tara flinched away from him, trembling with an emotion she couldn't fathom. Again she suspected him of teasing her and tried to warn herself to keep calm. Yet she had to mistrust the devil which seemed to be lurking behind the damped-down glitter in his eyes as they roved over her. Since they had first met he had had no compunction about looking his fill. If they had known each other longer she might have thought he was interested, but he had only first seen her a few hours ago.

But for all she strove to keep such sensible thoughts well to the fore, she felt a renewal of the odd excitement which had gone through her when he had touched her previously. This time he was only making contact with his eyes, and then mockingly, but she could still feel it affecting her. If he was making what was commonly known as a pass at her, he would find her far from co-operative! Not even for Jonathan's sake would she go that far!

'You appear to regard women in rather a strange light, Mr Voulgaris,' she managed coldly, at last.

'Why?' He appeared genuinely puzzled. 'Simply because I am honest enough to admit the sort of women I am interested in? Perhaps it would be better if you were equally frank regarding yourself, my dear. If I do no more than look at you, during the day or two we shall be together, then you might feel as insulted as you did when I referred to your appetite. We are simply talking of an appetite of a different kind. Some girls . . .'

'Mr Voulgaris!' furiously Tara jumped to her feet, 'I not only feel insulted—I refuse to remain on your yacht another minute!' Wild colour suffused her cheeks and her green eyes sparkled with the force of her anger. 'I wonder that your Greek women have any virtue left with men like you around! You're supposed to be looking after me, yet you're practically asking me to go to bed with you! Well, let me tell you I've never done such a thing in my life. Nor would I until I loved and married a man. The sort of relationship you refer to is—is positively indecent! Your wife . . .'

'I haven't got one, you little she-cat!' He was up beside her, interrupting her, his face as angry as her own. But where Tara's was rose-red and stormy, his was cold with contempt. 'If I have a bad opinion of women how do you think I came by it? And I'd advise you not to be too smug about sex. It is true that if two people care about each other they can be very righteous about it, but there are different kinds of caring, Miss Curtis. Is a man to deny himself because he doesn't experience this love you speak of so confidently? How does he know that it even exists? By the time a little romantic like yourself discovers it doesn't she could be too old to attract a man in any way.'

'You'd want me to settle for second best at my age?'

'I wasn't asking you to settle for anything,' his voice was still savage. 'To me you're just a beautiful, shapely little foreign girl, and I've met quite a few. I was merely amusing myself, if you like. Satisfying my curiosity. Another woman might have said yes or no without making such a drama of it. You intrigued me more than most, Tara Curtis, from the first moment I saw you, but I don't usually force a girl against her will.'

'Not—usually . . . ?'

'By heavens, young woman,' he declared tightly, 'must

you have everything in black and white! Never have I even attempted to use force, but one of these days I just might!'

'It was your fault!' She glared back at him, never pausing for a moment to wonder why two strangers should be quarrelling so violently, or why his icy calm should egg her on. 'All your fault,' she stammered. 'You, with your talk of sex!'

'I mentioned it once,' he corrected grimly, 'but while we're on the subject, I should perhaps advise you to consider it with caution, Miss Curtis. There is much passion in you, which I don't think you're yet aware of. A little warning, given in time, might prevent you from one day being swept off your feet. Which would be much against all these grand principles you are over proud of, would it not?'

His hands came down on her shoulders, giving her a small shake as he finished, the strength of his fingers biting into her tender skin indicating that he considered she deserved to be slapped.

Incensed, she struggled, lifting her hands to try and free herself from his grip. 'No man could ever do that to me,' she cried. 'Like all men you talk a lot of nonsense!'

He had goaded her and expected her to endure it but he was a man, a Greek, and he wouldn't put up with the same thing from a woman. Too late, Tara realised she had been foolish to express her feelings so wildly. His hold tightened, she felt his breath warm on her cheek as he muttered something in Greek beneath it. Then his mouth came nearer and his lips were on hers.

Her heart was pounding, violently against her chest, her body suddenly limp, completely helpless as his mouth crushed hers into submission. His arms tightened as they slipped completely around her as the kiss continued. She felt encompassed with fire, multi-coloured sensations which whirled her round in a dizzying spiral until the blood seemed to be rushing madly through her very veins.

When he released her she would have fallen if he had not steadied her immediately. He had kissed her hard and brutally, until a thousand stars had shattered in her head. Until he had wrung from her, without mercy, the kind of response which proved beyond doubt the truth of what he had been trying to tell her.

When Tara opened dazed eyes he was watching her darkly. 'That might begin to show you the error of your ways,' he said softly.

'My ways?' She wasn't to know that the glance she gave him was as bewildered as a child's.

'Your way of thinking,' he amended coolly, 'your foolishness in judging so presumptuously the feelings of others.'

She moved slightly, pushing away from him as the strength returned to her shaking limbs. 'It was scarcely—feelings we were talking about,' she managed to whisper.

'Passion, then!' he exclaimed harshly, and she felt a dark shock as his eyes glittered derisively. 'I'm merely trying to spare your pride.'

'I didn't get the impression you were trying to spare me anything!'

'It's time to adjust your way of thinking, then,' he drawled dryly, 'but I shouldn't hurry, if I were you. It will be a long time, I'm thinking, before your reactions are those of a grown woman. I'd advise you to to seek your bed now, Tara Curtis, and I do assure you it won't be necessary to lock your door.'

Not a grown woman, was the first thought to enter her head next morning, when she woke up. It was as if she had been repeating it all night, for it was there on her lips when she opened her eyes, lingering on the tip of her tongue, like a nasty taste in her mouth she couldn't get rid of. Last night, after leaving Damon Voulgaris, she had flown down to her cabin in a panicky temper. If there had been something behind her temper, a tremulous, aching

sensation, she had striven to ignore it. She had thrown
the few clothes she had unpacked into her suitcase. Snatching it up, she had rushed out again, to leave the boat, and
crashed straight into the hard arms of the very man she
had hoped to avoid.

'Where do you think you are going?' he had asked
curtly, instantly removing the suitcase from her startled
hands.

'I'm leaving ...'

'Don't be such a little fool!' he had exclaimed harshly,
literally picking her up and carrying her back to her cabin.
He had almost thrown her on to her bed, then, without
one further glance or word, he had left, locking the door.

A child, a little fool, he had called her, all in the space
of an hour or two. Bitterly Tara wondered if there could
be anything else.

The door had remained locked most of the night, for at
regular intervals, before the boat sailed, she had tried it.
Curiously she gazed at it, trying to forget the arms and
the long, lithe strides of the man who had borne her
through it. Was it still locked this morning? As they must
be well away from land there wouldn't be much point.

No sooner had these thoughts crossed her mind than
there came a knock. 'Come in,' she called, after a hesitant
moment, clutching the sheet beneath her chin, fully expecting it to be Voulgaris.

It wasn't. It was the steward, Georgios, carrying a tray.
'Mr Voulgaris felt you would be hungry, miss. He has
sent your breakfast.'

'Oh!' Her voice far from appreciative, Tara stared
at him. So, not content with his former jibes, Voulgaris was
doing his best to make common knowledge of her appetite.
A joke was a joke, but he was going too far! Last night
she had scarcely eaten all day, not for several days, really,
because of excitement and nervousness. He must have
guessed this, but he still continued to taunt her. 'You can
take it away,' she recklessly instructed a bewildered

Georgios. 'You can tell Mr Voulgaris I don't want it.'

Immediately the man backed out, she regretted what seemed now a rather foolish gesture of defiance. It could only result in one of two things. Either Voulgaris would thunder in here and throw it at her, or he would ignore what she had done as a rather foolish tantrum and let her go hungry. He wouldn't realise, she sighed morosely, how, at almost twenty-two, it rankled to be constantly dubbed an adolescent! Was it her fault she hadn't had the time or opportunity for the affairs which might have added the sophistication he obviously considered she required to elevate her to the superior status of a woman?

A few minutes passed and all was quiet. With a sigh of what she took to be relief, Tara threw off the silken sheets which so sensuously covered her body and eased herself with luxurious slowness on to the edge of the bed. How lovely not having to scramble out in the dawn light with half a million chores in front of her and only a day to get through them. A cup of coffee wouldn't have come amiss, though.

Ruefully she was just putting this thought from her when the door flew open, helped by a foot, and Damon Voulgaris crashed in, carrying the tray she had impulsively rejected. She had an uneasy feeling it was the first time he had ever performed such a menial task in his life and that his role pleased him no better than it pleased her!

As he bore down on her there was no time to grasp a wrap or to hide herself again under the sheets. Instead, with a startled gasp, she clutched her arms around her somewhat old-fashioned nightdress and stared at him defiantly.

He put the tray down so emphatically that the silver coffee pot actually bounced. Turning to her, his face like granite, he said, 'If you don't eat this, *thespinis*, I'll return and force it down you. Do you want the whole crew speculating on your foolish tantrums?'

There! Hadn't she known he would use such a phrase!

'If——' she stammered, 'if you call me childish once
more, Mr Voulgaris, I might jump overboard!'

'So that rankled, did it?' he observed, with cruel frank-
ness. 'If you jumped overboard, Miss Curtis, I should
feel fully justified in all my opinions.'

It was almost as if he was saying he wouldn't mind
seeing the last of her, and she found herself shrinking back
from the anger she felt sure was brewing. Very conscious
of his lean and powerful body, she stared at him. This
morning he wore a pair of blue jeans and a white tee-shirt,
which seemed to emphasise every inch of his well muscled
figure. Tara swallowed, as something alien hit her, and
looked away. Unable to sustain his calculating glance any
longer, she shivered, directing her eyes towards the porthole.

'You tremble, Miss Curtis?' His voice reached her
ears, the softly vibrant tones affecting her oddly. 'You can
scarcely be cold in this warm cabin, especially in that ser-
viceable nightgown you are wearing.'

'That's——' she had been about to say it was her own
business, when she remembered her unwashed face, her
sleep-rumpled hair, which she hadn't yet thought to run
a comb through. In another moment he would be accusing
her of being slovenly, along with everything else! Feeling
her colour rising, her hands flew to her cheeks, leaving to
full view the nightdress he apparently deplored. It was
one her mother had loaned her. Mrs Curtis had pointed
out that it might be wise to take something sensible as a
cheap taverna probably didn't have locks on the doors, but
while it was too big for Tara it didn't entirely hide the
attractions of the shape underneath.

The interest in his eyes, mixed as it was with hard
impatience, almost proved the last straw. She sidetracked,
leaving her sentence unfinished, beginning another without apology. 'I'm sorry you don't approve of my clothes,
Mr Voulgaris. I haven't travelled, but my mother has. Per-

haps she had a reason for ensuring that I came to Greece sensibly dressed.'

'I don't doubt it,' he replied, so dryly that her colour deepened. His eyes, coming back to her face, stilled her sharp retort before it could be uttered. As on the previous evening, she felt caught and held by something frightening but wholly intangible. Something beyond the ordinary scheme of things.

He looked down on her with glints of speculation in his eyes as if seeking, without even touching her, to hold her captive. So real was the sensation, so terrible, that an extraordinary relief flooded through her when surprisingly he turned away.

'When you have finished your breakfast and dressed, Tara, I will see you on deck. There are things I wish to say to you.'

The light was like honey, clearest gold in the rising sun. The air was cool but not cold, exhilarating yet with a hint of warmth to come. The yacht cut cleanly through the blue water and a shower of silver sea-spray was like a splash of sparkling cologne, salt-wet and refreshing.

Bracing herself against the rail, her face tilted, breathing deeply, Tara was conscious of excitement as the deck moved under her feet. There came to her a sense of freedom which she had never experienced before. Perhaps it was to do with the open sea, the tang of salt in the wind? She only knew it was glorious and seemed to be bringing her wholly alive. She felt the stirrings of a vitality she hadn't known she possessed, a secret longing to cast all her long-formed inhibitions aside and live recklessly. Here, with the wind in her long hair, whipping her cheeks to a glorious colour, she felt wrapped in a pagan world of her own, entirely enchanted.

When Damon Voulgaris joined her, a little later, she wished he had left her alone to enjoy it. What she was feeling she felt sure could not be shared. A moment ago she had been alone with the elements, unfettered, free. With Damon Voulgaris by her side she found she could no longer concentrate on the sea and sun, the vivid spectacular clarity of colour. His was a too disturbing influence. Beside him even the shrill calls of the sea-birds faded. He seemed to steal every scrap of attention away from these other things she had found so absorbing.

Try as she might to ignore him, at least until he spoke to her, her eyes came back. She met his and there was a peculiar tenseness between them, fleeting but not comfortable.

On her part, Tara told herself, it must stem from his treatment of her last night. Perhaps she had asked for all she had got by objecting to being called a child. Yet, when he treated her as an adult, she felt the outcome had startled them both. Not that a man like Damon Voulgaris would be startled in the same way as she, but she had sensed he had been—surprised.

What, she wondered, rather hysterically, would he say if she were to confess herself so innocent that, while she had scarcely kissed a man until last night, it hadn't been that particular kind of innocence she'd had in mind? It had been her guilty conscience regarding what Jonathan had asked her to do which had reared its ugly head each time Damon Voulgaris had called her childish and naïve. They just hadn't been thinking of the same thing! Somehow, it had seemed to Tara that if Damon Voulgaris ever discovered her deception, it wouldn't seem so far to fall if she could prevent him putting her on too high a pedestal. Not, she brooded darkly, that he would place many women on one of those! He had seen too much, he was too cynical.

Vaguely, as she half drowned in the glittering depth of his dark eyes, Tara wondered if she could make her position clearer, without condemning herself altogether. They might not be so long in reaching Polos, there might not be another chance.

'Mr Voulgaris . . . ?'

'Make it Damon,' he suggested quietly.

'Oh!' Everything she had been trying to say flew out of her head. She glanced at him quickly, so obviously trying to gauge his mood that he laughed.

'You find it so difficult, Tara, after last night?'

'Oh,' she said again, her cheeks pink, 'that was a mistake, you shouldn't remind me. Not that the mistake was mine!' she exclaimed fiercely.

'Don't you think you should leave it?' he smiled, though his eyes were searching. 'I went too far, too fast, but I don't intend apologising.'

Tara wasn't sure she liked the sound of that, either! It seemed a wayward streak in her must ignore his advice and take up where they had left off. She didn't intend discussing a kiss, of course, or anything remotely connected, but she recalled how he had had the nerve, in his vastly superior manner, to read her a lecture! 'You told me,' she said scornfully, 'that Greeks are very circumspect!'

He looked at her, mockery gleaming in his eyes. 'Come, Tara, let us air all your grievances, for it seems until we do none of us can be at peace. Greek men may all be different, but none of us are bound by quite the same rules which govern our women. I have actually lived less in Greece during the past few years than in other countries. I am much travelled, Tara, and much disillusioned. I think I have become the kind of man who takes what he wants, but that isn't quite the same as taking everything which comes his way.'

'I should think quite a few women come your way, because that's what you're talking about, isn't it?'

'Maybe, but I don't think you have to worry about any other woman, Tara.'

His voice was oddly gentle. She had the rather confusing idea he was trying to tell her something. Something, judging from the accompanying narrowing of his eyes, that he was as yet strangely unsure of himself about. He must be speaking idly, as there could be nothing personal in his words, despite the fact that he had kissed her and treated her roughly. They hadn't known each other twenty-four hours. The peculiar crackling tension between them was merely an intangible sign of the dislike they felt for each other.

Trying to speak lightly, Tara looked away from him. 'You don't have to be tactful. I wouldn't dream of criticising your friends. After all, I don't even know them and, after reaching Polos this evening I don't suppose we shall see each other again.'

He said, just as casually, his eyes on the proud tilt of her chin, 'I'm afraid you won't reach Polos this evening. You distracted me, but this was what I wished to speak to you about.'

'Not reach Polos?' She wasn't sure she could have heard properly. 'But you promised!'

'I did no such thing,' he contradicted, his glance hardening again as he met the rising indignation in her eyes. 'I agreed with your brother to bring you there safely, nothing more.'

She strove to keep calm, which wasn't easy. 'I suppose if it just means another night . . .'

'I'm afraid it might be about four days. I have to call at a couple of islands.'

'If only you'd said!' she cut in angrily. 'Four days! I could have stayed in Athens and caught the ferry this morning.'

'I didn't know until we'd sailed,' he said shortly, his eyes glinting dangerously, as though he disliked being taken to task by anyone, especially a woman.

'What about my brother and sister-in-law?' Her chest heaved, drawing his eyes speculatively. 'They'll be expecting me.'

'I've been in touch with Tim,' Damon Voulgaris vouched suavely. 'He is quite content as he wasn't sure if you would come at all. Another day or two, and these are his own words, won't make any difference.'

Completely unconvinced, Tara frowned unhappily. It wasn't only her late arrival she was worried about. It was having to stay longer in Damon Voulgaris's company. A cruise, even a short one, on a luxury yacht like this would be a prospect a lot would never dream of turning down, but all Tara felt was a terrible apprehension—a kind of nameless dread, she had never experienced before, not even at the height of her father's illness. She couldn't understand it, but it must mean something. It might be because of Damon Voulgaris's connection with Greg Golden. Voulgaris was the last man on earth she wanted to be indebted to, but somehow she sensed it went deeper than that.

'I can't stay, Mr Voulgaris.' Panic gave her voice firmness while another thought, an embarrassing one, this time, made it tremble again. 'Besides . . .'

As she trailed off and her cheeks flushed, he smiled dryly. 'I know exactly what you're trying to say, but we don't happen to be on the boat by ourselves. I've a crew who make adequate chaperons.'

'Perhaps they've had adequate practice!'

'Perhaps.' He seemed more amused than disconcerted, and, in sudden rage, Tara read into his brief admission all that was bad.

'I'll get off at the first island we come to,' she exclaimed sharply, 'and make my own way to Polos. There's sure to be a ferry.'

'Listen, *thespinis*!' As though no longer able to resist an inclination to shake her, his hands shot out to grasp her bare arms. 'I don't know if you deliberately set out to provoke me. I might be tempted to call your bluff, but first let's get this thing straight! I promised your brother I'd deliver you personally, so there won't be any more attempts to escape. Last night I almost made sure you wouldn't try again, so take warning. Next time I won't be so gentle with you, my small antagonist. Next time don't expect me to be gentle at all!'

There was a darkness in his eyes as he snapped shut his expressive mouth, the darkness of threat, a smouldering of anger which froze every word of protest. Tara shivered.

Feeling it, his face smoothed into lines of grim satisfaction. 'Whatever I want from you, Tara Curtis, it is not retaliation. I don't wish to be peppered with sharp words and even sharper glances. Take my advice, young woman, think of the next few days as the kind of break most girls of your age would appreciate. Boats can be fun and very pleasant. I prefer a smaller one which I own and can sail myself, but I'm not averse to being a gentleman of leisure occasionally, in the right company.'

She flashed him a glance of pure hate. 'I refuse to make any promises, Mr Voulgaris.'

'Damon,' he insisted emphatically, thrusting her suddenly away from him. 'Say it!'

'Damon ...' she repeated after him weakly, wholly astonished that she dared not disobey.

His laughter was brief, without humour. 'Just remember this little incident, Tara, while making your first plans of escape. Recall what I can make you do with only a very little willpower.'

When he left her to go down below again, Tara stared after him in despair. What did she, or rather, what could she do now? How was she to spend the next few days alone with such a man? Hadn't Tim realised what he was doing? Surely he could have made some alternative arrangements? Bitterness welled up. Maybe, as Damon Voulgaris said, many girls would appreciate such a situation, but she just wasn't one of them! Never had she felt more deserted in her life. Tim ought to have asserted himself! It occurred to Tara that, confronted by a man like Damon Voulgaris, neither of her brothers might lift a finger to help her, and, because her hands were tied, she could scarcely do a thing to help herself.

This needn't prevent her, though, from leaving the yacht if she got the chance. If Voulgaris had arranged to to see someone he would have to put into land, some harbour somewhere, and while he went to keep his appointment she would be left by herself. If she appeared acquiescent he would believe she had accepted her fate and his suspicions might be lulled. Anything was worth trying rather than staying here!

They passed Kea, only forty nautical miles from Piraeus. Damon, never far from her side, leant against the rails and told her the island was a place of peace and tranquillity, of quiet beauty. There people fished and grew oranges and lemons. They kept sheep and cattle and goats. It was a place of ancient monasteries and famous ruins, typical of most of the islands which dotted these beautiful seas. Often he had dropped anchor in Kea's St Nicholas Bay. When Tara asked if they were not going to visit the island that day, he said no, they must go on.

For the rest of the afternoon Damon was occupied and the evening was uneventful. He was curiously evasive as to their exact destination and some instinct warned Tara that he didn't want her to know of it until they arrived. It would be a waste of time trying to find out. He did give the impression that he wouldn't be averse to answering questions about the islands generally, but such was the growing apprehension and resentment in Tara's heart that she maintained a stubborn silence. If he refused to enlighten her then she must just look for someone who would.

With this in mind she approached a sailor, next morning, as he worked on deck. She walked up to him smiling as it suddenly occurred to her that a friend might be useful. The young man spoke English, which surprised her until she realised that naturally Vougaris's crew would be bilingual as he used the yacht mostly for entertaining.

This man was young, pleasant to look at, but not noticeably willing to talk to her. He answered her few queries about his work slowly, to begin with, and with some reluctance. Feeling desperately in need of an ally, some-one she might appeal to for assistance, Tara kept smiling at him until, after a very few minutes, he was laughing with her merrily. His name was Myron, she discovered, and he lived at Lamia, in Central Greece.

'I should like to hear about your home,' she said eagerly, genuinely interested, squatting down beside him as he paused in his scrubbing of the deck, prepared to listen.

A voice behind her spoke sharply and a hand yanked her unmercifully to her feet. 'Tara! Would you kindly explain what you think you are doing?'

The sailor smiled nervously, a grin which quickly dis-appeared after a few curt words from Damon Voulgaris in Greek. He replied apologetically and went below.

'Did you have to be so beastly to him?' she cried angrily, wrenching her arm from Damon's harsh grip. 'I couldn't understand what you were saying, but it didn't sound nice.'

Equally angry, he regained his hurting hold of her arm, sweeping her along, not letting go of her until he'd dumped her, indignation and all, on one of the chaise-longues which was out on the sun-deck. It was soft, but the way he thrust her on to it almost hurt. 'I don't feel particularly nice at the moment, young woman,' he warned grimly. 'Just sit there and shut up and listen to me!'

CHAPTER THREE

FURIOUSLY Tara gathered her sprawling limbs into a more dignified position as she stared up at him. It was obvious that she was going to be read a lecture which she had no particular inclination to listen to. With a touch of insolence she hadn't known she possessed, she cried, 'I don't know what you're getting in such a state about! What I do doesn't concern you. I'm a big girl now, if you hadn't noticed, and quite able to look after myself!'

Damon Voulgaris's eyes swept over her with an insolence which went beyond anything Tara had expressed. 'I'd noticed,' he replied with grim dryness. 'And if you hadn't been my guest I'd have no compunction about leaving you to your fate. You were smiling and flirting with that man like a small tramp. A sailor, madam, is human as well as useful. You were asking to be assaulted.'

'Why, you——!' Tara gasped with humiliation. Recklessly she hissed, 'I suppose you're the only man who's allowed to be human around here. The night before last you didn't hesitate when you—when you ...'

'Yes?' he asked derisively, his eyes on her mouth with such deliberation that she was left in no doubt that, for all his prompting, he knew exactly what she was talking about.

'Don't you realise, Tara,' he said shortly, after allowing her a few moments of discomfort, 'that if that man was to discover that you and I had just met, that you were, in fact, merely the sister of an ordinary taverna keeper to whom I was giving a lift, you wouldn't be safe.'

'Not safe?' she spluttered, flushing hotly under his insults. 'You must exaggerate. This is your yacht.'

'Agreed,' he nodded suavely. 'But when we reach Polos

41

it might be there for several days and I can scarcely confine my men to their quarters. They are allowed free time.'

Tara had heard of girls who encouraged men too freely while they were abroad, but she didn't want him to know the real reason she had smiled so warmly at the young sailor. 'I'm sorry,' she whispered, lowering her lashes, hoping a proper show of penitence might deceive Damon Voulgaris more easily than temper had done.

Only a slight hardening of his dark features betrayed the fact that he wasn't at all taken in by her sudden change of tactics. 'Just because I smiled at the man!' she began defensively.

'Smile at me, Tara,' Damon Voulgaris interrupted curtly, dropping down by her side, with his hand going under her averted chin to turn her face back to him. 'It might be safer. You're very lovely, more so when you smile, and I don't mind if you—go to my head a little.'

'Because you will easily forget me?'

His thumb lightly sketched her uncertain mouth. 'I will answer that better after I've said goodbye to you.'

She drew a quick breath, careless for a second, that he heard it. The touch of his hand caressing her throat was curious. It was sending shafts of fire down through her body, an odd, melting sensation through her veins. She felt so burnt she flinched, not welcoming the effect he seemed to have on her, especially after his last careless remark. 'It might be appropriate to say, Mr Voulgaris, that we are indeed like ships which pass in the night.'

He smiled, while obviously not appreciating her wry humour. A smouldering darkness at the back of his eyes gave the impression that it was he who would decide exactly where and when they parted. His hands left her and he stood up. Because she had expected him to leave her she was surprised to hear him saying, 'Why don't you stop fighting me, Tara Curtis, and go and find your swimsuit? I'm sure you have one. Then we can just sit here, on deck, and enjoy the sunshine.'

For the rest of the day, until evening, Tara did as she was told and relaxed. At first she felt guilty about it, not being used to being so idle. Because of her father her periods of leisure had been brief, and the feeling that she ought to be doing something was difficult to throw off. The sun, at this time of the year, was still hot and out of her jeans and shirt she felt cooler and enjoyed the feel of the light wind blowing over her bare skin. She only regretted her bikini wasn't new. She hadn't used it since her father was taken ill, over three years ago. Now it seemed too tight in certain places, too slack in others. She wished she had tried it on before leaving home, but as it had scarcely been worn she hadn't thought of doing so. There wouldn't have been money to spare for a new one anyway.

Damon Voulgaris, stretched out beside her, was a further cause for embarrassment. She had received a jolt on first seeing him wearing only a dark pair of trunks.

That he didn't appear to share her embarrassment seemed absolute confirmation that the circles he usually moved in were sophisticated to the extreme. Every hard muscle of his powerful body seemed to stand out and she closed her eyes to obliterate such blatant evidence of his superb masculinity. But even behind closed lids she could still see the smoothness of his healthy tan, the roughness of dark hair curling on his broad chest. Her pulse raced and she shivered.

For a long while he lay indolent by her side, his hand resting lightly on her arm. Tara had been about to shake it off when she suddenly discovered she liked it there. It started up all the odd feelings again, but, as she grew used to it, instead of being frightened she found it tantalised. Holding her breath, almost as if on the verge of a great revelation, she lay still.

Later Damon invited her to go swimming and, because she fancied he might be laughing at her simplicity, she eagerly agreed. He had the captain stop the boat while they dived overboard.

Tara had once won cups for swimming and, though very much out of practice, was still in a class of her own.

'You're very good!' he teased mockingly, as she cut cleanly through the water beside him, 'Not many girls can swim like a fish.'

'Perhaps I'm showing off, Mr Voulgaris,' she retorted pertly.

'Mr Voulgaris?' He turned his face darkly towards her, his eyebrows raised.

'Mr Voulgaris,' she repeated, an imp of unconscious provocation dancing in her green eyes, which blended so subtly with the blueness of the water.

He trod water suddenly, catching her to him in full view of several members of the crew who were watching, and kissing her. His mouth crushed hers briefly then he raised his head. 'My name!' he demanded, his eyes on her bruised lips, 'or else!'

'Damon,' she gulped, all fight going out of her. She didn't dare risk exposing herself to his last threat.

'And smile,' he commanded, 'when you speak to me. If I'm to protect you we must give the impression that we are something more than strangers.'

Her hair floated on the water, she wasn't sure where her body was. She was sure that the urge to wrap herself in Damon Voulgaris's arms and sink to the bottom didn't belong to her. The reckless, sensuous being who had invaded her body had nothing to do with Tara Curtis, who must be renowned for her good sense and respectability. She tried to obey the order to smile, but it wasn't until her second attempt that she succeeded.

When they climbed back on board Georgios, the steward, offered her his hand and the engines throbbed back to life. Damon ordered coffee and Georgios hurried away, as did the rest of the men. Tara was suddenly too conscious of Damon standing over her, wrapping her in a towel. Water was streaming through the dark hair on his chest and down his powerful legs. There was, suddenly, too much of him!

As he placed a casual hand under her elbow, turning her back towards the loungers, she felt the familiar feeling of warmth rush through her, removing the momentary chill from her limbs. How was it, she wondered unhappily, that each time he touched her she became more aware of him?

He had warned her she must make people believe they weren't strangers, but this seemed no explanation for how she was beginning to feel whenever he looked at her in a certain way. The sooner she was away from him the better, and the way her heart beat as he settled her gently, this time, on her chaise-longue only strengthened her determination to escape him.

He was considering her now very closely and she flushed, drawing the towel tightly around her damp body. 'I think I should go below and change.'

His mouth quirked. 'The sun will soon dry you,' he replied, 'if you give it a chance. And I like what you are wearing better than a lot of the other clothes you have.'

'You haven't seen them all,' she said stiffly, ignoring his dry hint and huddling deeper in her towel.

'I've seen a sample.'

'People don't dress so very smartly nowadays,' she mumbled, trying not to feel depressed. She understood only too well, that the smart set he moved in would probably not be seen dead in the things she wore.

'You're more attractive than most,' he said bluntly, glancing at her cynically. 'You should learn to cash in on your good looks. In your position most girls wouldn't hesitate.'

'Is that advice, scorn, or wishful thinking?' she asked furiously.

'All right, Miss Curtis—my apologies, calm down.' His white teeth glinted. 'I don't believe I've come across your kind before, not outside Greece. Your tongue is too sharp, my girl. It's a good job there are—other things about you I like better.'

Regardless of her stiff little shrug, he reached for the towel with which she was drying her hair. 'Here, let me do that. You can't dry your hair and keep yourself covered at the same time, and this you appear to think necessary.'

'It's all right, I can manage.'

He took no notice. 'I have a fancy to help. Stop making a fuss, Tara.'

To enable her to endure the feel of his hands on her head, she said slowly, 'You don't sound so very Greek when you speak like that.'

His hand rested on her nape, ignoring her tense reaction. 'I'm only half Greek actually. My mother was English, like yourself, but I was brought up in Greece. It is my country, no matter how far my business takes me away from it.'

'Is your mother still alive?' Tara felt somewhat startled.

'Yes, but after my father died she married again and went back to London. She married an Englishman this time, so unless I'm in London. I don't see much of her.'

What had begun as an idle question now held Tara's interest wholly. 'Are you like her?'

He laughed. 'No way. She's very fair. Fairer than you, I think,' his hand ruffled her hair as though he was considering it. 'I believe it was her fairness which attracted my father in the first place, but she does not have your depth of colouring or your beautiful green eyes. Fairness can be very insipid, *thespinis,* but I don't think you're made that way at all. I rather think the force of your feelings would be strong enough to sweep everything else aside, once you learn how to deal with that intensely puritan streak in your nature.'

'How can you know?' Tara gasped, hating the way his voice, his words could seem as potent as a kiss. He was pushing the towel gently aside from her shoulders, softly caressing her smooth skin which was warming under the heat of the sun. She knew she should push him away, but his touch was becoming like a drug. Reluctantly she had tasted it, now she wanted more. He was tall, broad-shouldered, a powerful figure of a man and very handsome, and she was terrified she wouldn't be able to keep on resisting him. She was too aware of him. She could feel a certain tenseness between them and instinctively she knew he felt it, too. 'How can you know?' she repeated indignantly, when he didn't reply.

'This way, you little stupid!' The faint smile on his lips faded as he lowered his mouth gently to hers and brushed the towel completely away from her. Holding her mouth captive, he slipped an arm around her bare shoulders, pulling her up to him while his other hand went lightly over her breast.

No one had ever touched her so intimately before and the sensation alarmed her. She flinched, drawing a sharp breath, while her hands had the crazy desire to clutch him tightly yet push him away. Her head jerked back in incredible fright as the wild emotion suddenly consuming her trembling body made her want to cry out. He must have felt her fear but refused to pander to it as the sensuous pressure of his mouth and hands merely deepened. When he released her, seconds later, her face was hot, as though burnt by the flames of the fire which rampaged inside her.

'You asked a silly question, you insisted on an answer. You got it,' he stated calmly. 'That surely explains everything you wanted to know.'

Because her heart was still racing too hard for comfort she could only stare at him. The relief of seeing him retreat to his own lounger was mixed with a bleak feeling of desertion. If only she had been more sophisticated mightn't he have gone on making love to her instead of casting her aside, as if she were a novice who must be initiated slowly?

Georgios arrived with their coffee and, ashamed of her thoughts, Tara jerked her eyes from Damon Voulgaris's hooded ones, conscious that he was probably reading her mind too clearly. Her colour, which had receded, returned and she was glad to pour the coffee to give her something to do with her hands, although she regretted their shaking. Quickly impatient that she should allow Damon Voulgaris to affect her like this, she ignored his remark, going back, impulsively, to the safer subject of his mother. She must remember how she disliked this man! 'How did your parents meet?'

His eyes, when she dared another glance at him, still rested on her. Momentarily she trembled, but he replied coolly enough, 'We are in shipping. The men who run such companies usually get around. My father also enjoyed a good social life, although I believe the war curtailed it somewhat. It was during the war that he met my mother. I was born apparently from a love match in the early nineteen-forties.'

'I see.' Lowering her long, curling lashes to hide the flicker in her green eyes, Tara added, with a forced lightness, 'You sound very sceptical about love, Damon.'

His smile twisted. 'Perhaps because I suspect it is used too often as an excuse to indulge other, less admirable, though not to say less enjoyable, emotions.'

Tara was surprised to see a certain darkness settle over his strong features, as if he were recalling something—or someone—whom he distrusted. Whatever it was, he appeared to put it immediately from him, but, feeling cold and hit by a sudden depression, Tara drew her towel closely around herself again.

'Leave it,' he said impatiently, misjudging her defensive action. 'Haven't I told you, you don't need to be so modest with looks like yours. Learn to enjoy the sunshine.'

Tara didn't protest. She couldn't tell him the real reason why, this time, she sought the protection of her towel, but obediently she discarded it. While it wasn't easy to ignore the attention he bent on her she had an idea he was really far away, somewhere where she couldn't possibly reach him. After a few minutes, when she made some excuse and went to her cabin, he didn't seem to even notice her going.

For dinner that evening she wore a pale silky skirt and top and found herself regretting that she had not brought more clothes. Wryly she assured herself it wasn't anything to worry about. At the taverna she would probably be kept too busy to have the opportunity of wearing anything but an overall. It would be a far cry from living on a luxurious yacht like this! As she brushed her gleaming hair with a rather feverish vigour she hoped urgently that they would soon reach Polos as every day seemed to be more unsettling. Her emotions, alternating as they were between eagerness and fear, were becoming far from comfortable to live with.

Damon, as usual, was dressed formally and she wondered if he would still have dressed this way if she hadn't been with him. Even in evening dress he looked tough and powerful and, as she walked into the salon, she experienced an almost physical shock at the sight of him. The tension between them smouldered again and she wished desperately that she knew what it was about. Never before had she felt as if she was joined to someone by electric wires and, worse than this, that they might snap in a devastating explosion on one false move on her part.

This feeling bred so fine an apprehension that she scarcely touched the wine he poured during the meal they shared.

'What's troubling you, Tara?'

She hadn't been aware he was watching her so closely and she shivered. He never missed a thing. 'I was just wondering about Polos,' she prevaricated, trying to speak evenly. 'I mean, Tim's bound to be wondering . . .'

The flash in Damon's eyes was unexplainable. 'What makes you think so? I told you I had spoken to him. He doesn't expect us until we arrive. Certainly he won't be wasting time wondering!'

'Are you usually so sure of yourself, of your facts, Mr—
I mean, Damon?' she asked sullenly.

'Usually,' he answered imperturbably. 'Which is more
than you appear to be.' He paused, smiling suddenly, so
she was enveloped by the charm of him. 'I would like it
better if you spent these few days concentrating on me,
rather than worrying about your brother. Don't you feel it
is a good chance, Tara Curtis, for us to get to know each
other?'

It might be that, she thought dully, but there could be
no point in it. Stubbornly she kept her mind away from
his tantalising suggestion. 'Do you always take your yacht
to the island?' she asked innocently, and was unprepared
for the wary tightening of his jawbone.

'Not very often.'

'I should have thought it the wrong time of year?'

'Oh,' he smiled grimly. 'And you're an authority on
such matters? I assure you you are quite safe. An experienced seaman can read the water, Tara, like the back of his
hand. It is one of the tricks of the trade and I have sailed
in far worse seas than anything you will see here during
the next few weeks.'

'Of course.' She flushed, staring down at her *kedonia*,
little Greek clams on the half shell. Suddenly it came
to her that he might be taking Greg Golden sailing. He
might even intend hiding him on the yacht and might naturally be suspicious if she showed an undue interest in his
activities on Polos. She felt so dismayed by this that she
sat for a few minutes without speaking. If this was so she
might never get the information which Jonathan was after.
As she stared down at her clams she was sure she should
feel ashamed of the relief which ran through her.

'A penny for them?' Damon asked softly, relenting.

'Not for sale.' She lifted her flower-like face and smiled
at him, the relief she was feeling making a radiance of her
eyes.

She heard his breath rasp, but her feeling of wellbeing

went beyond taking this in. It blossomed inside her, expanded, and her eyes shone. Never had she thought of her promise to Jonathan as a load on her back. Not until the possibility of getting rid of it, of having the responsibility of failure taken out of her hands, had she realised its dampening effect. Jonathan couldn't possibly blame her if, through no fault of her own, she never set eyes on Greg Golden. He would be disappointed, but something else was bound to turn up.

Startled, she became aware of Damon Voulgaris leaning over the table and taking her hand. He played gently with her fingers before turning her hand over. Deliberately, as she half held her breath, he raised it, pressing his mouth to the softness of her palm.

Breathlessly she tugged it away, after an appreciable moment, not understanding the sharp little thrill which ran through her, which flashed up her arm, parting her lips so that his eyes narrowed quickly on them and the tension rose between them again until she almost screamed.

Apparently more experienced at this curious game than she was, he made no immediate attempt to recapture her hand, and Tara wondered if he deliberately set out to torture. She might have also wondered why she had used that particular word, if her mind hadn't been in such a turmoil. As she watched him regarding her thoughtfully, her cheeks went pale.

'Have you never had a lover, Tara?'

'No ...' Vaguely she knew she should be telling him to mind his own business, but there was a peculiar weakness in her, at that moment, that would deny him nothing.

'Why not?'

She wished he wouldn't persist. It disturbed her terribly. 'Do I have to have a reason?'

'Yes.' There was a kind of hard implacability about him, a ruthlessness of intention she had never met before. He held her eyes, demanding an answer. 'You must have had the opportunity, so there has to be a reason.'

She sighed, quite willing to be lost in his dark, kindling gaze but not sure what to say to him. 'Not all girls are promiscuous. I've never wanted to go to bed with a man, if that's what you're curious about. Maybe I'm not so cynical about love as you are.'

'Love!' his laughter was hard. 'You don't know what you are talking about, my dear Tara. It's simply, is it not, that no man has taken the trouble to arouse you?'

'I won't sit here and listen!' Breaking off because her voice quivered so much, she jumped angrily to her feet.

'Sit down!' he commanded curtly, and when to her own astonishment she obeyed, he said, 'You're so young and touchy! I wonder that your parents allowed you to come out here. With your indiscretion, Tara, you might easily have attracted a load of trouble.' He paused, in hard reflection, as she stared mutinously. 'Tim did say he had expected his father would come, perhaps both your parents. Why didn't they?'

Tara nervously gave a little shake of her head. 'Daddy has been ill.'

'All the more reason, I should have thought, why a holiday would have done him good.'

Georgios interrupted apologetically, with a discreet knock on the door. 'There is a message for you, sir. Will you take it?'

Murmuring a formal excuse, Damon departed. Tara suppressed her sigh of relief until the door had closed behind him. It wasn't that she had been particularly worried about his queries regarding her parents, she had been frightened he would return to his scornful contemplation of her virtue.

Wandering into the other salon, she noticed Georgios had left their coffee and poured herself a cup. As she stirred in sugar she wondered how soon she dared go to bed. It was still early, but she wasn't sure how much more of Damon Voulgaris she could take in such intimate surroundings. For all they saw of the crew they might have been completely alone on the yacht, and the thought filled her suddenly with a strange foreboding.

Voulgaris was away quite a while. When he did return she asked politely if she should ring for more coffee but he shook his head, pouring himself a drink instead. She could see his mood had changed, his eyes had gone hard and distant. If she hadn't known better she would have sworn he looked bleak, that whatever his message had been about, it hadn't been very welcome. With a bewildering surge of concern she had a strange urge to ask what was wrong, but remembered in time that, on such a short acquaintance, such a query might seem impertinent.

Frowning, he watched her as he drained his glass. 'I believe I have news which will please you,' he surprised her by saying dryly, at last. 'Tomorrow we reach Naxos and will leave for Polos by air.'

'Tomorrow?' Feeling slightly stunned, Tara looked away from the grey glance directed so intently on her. Where was the happiness which should have been flooding her, the relief? Relief was there, but the exact reason for that seemed obscured.

'What—nothing more to say?' His eyebrows rose. 'I imagined, at the very least, you'd be throwing your arms about me. Instead you appear somewhat bewildered.'

Too quickly she exclaimed, 'It will be so good to reach Polos.'

'Is this the best you can do?'

Because he taunted, she frowned. 'You say we leave by air?'

'Helicopter.'

Something about his tone stung her to challenge him, 'Why didn't you take a helicopter from Athens? This whole journey seems to have been a bit of a waste of time!'

His mouth tightened and her heart fluttered. He wasn't prepared to be tolerant. 'You aren't in a position to question any motive of mine, Miss Curtis, but, if it pleases you, you might be interested to know this is the first proper break I've had all summer. Not that it could be regarded as much of a break, what with one thing and another, but I was looking forward to a few relaxing days at sea.'

'Which I messed up. You don't have to spell it out, Mr Voulgaris, although I can't remember being described as "one thing and another" before!'

'No,' he smiled faintly, 'it wasn't that. I've enjoyed your company, even your contrariness, but something has cropped up.'

'Is it—anything I can help with?' She knew it was ridiculous to ask. While physically he didn't seem to object to having her near, mentally he kept her miles away. She had an insane, inexplicable desire to weep.

Mockingly his mouth twisted. 'If that's another way of asking the reason for curtailing my brief holiday, I'm afraid I can't tell you. It wouldn't do you any good to know.'

'Sorry I asked!' she retorted, with a flippancy designed both to annoy and hide her hurt. Perhaps she felt so flat because there could be no further need to plan an escape, no real necessity to fight Damon Voulgaris any more. She couldn't understand why, instead of happiness, the disposal of such problems brought only despair. A despair and sense of unhappiness which had her acting like a spoiled child!

'Tara!' He put down his glass and came over to her, laying soothing hands on her shoulders, as if he sensed the turmoil within. 'Don't let us ruin our friendship at this stage by foolish quarrels.'

'So you think I'm foolish?'

He sighed, and his hands tightened, obviously taking into account her white face. The trace of defiance he appeared to disregard, as if it was what lay under it which bothered him. 'It takes two to make a quarrel, Tara, but you aren't old enough to be sensible all the time. Everything just now is difficult ...'

'Will I see you on Polos?' It was out before she could

pull herself together or wonder at the incredibility of such a question.

'Perhaps. I'm not sure.' A shuttered expression came over his face, hardening the words which dropped from his lips so they hit her like so many icicles. He looked like a man driven by a need to restrain himself.

He was wiser than she, Tara decided bitterly, reading in his aloof withdrawal regret at having given any encouragement at all to someone like herself. To a girl who might, if she became insistent, prove an embarrassment on a small island. How could she have lowered her pride enough to make it seem it mattered that she saw him again? Hot with mortification, she flushed, pulling herself with determination from under his hands.

'Oh, well,' she laughed lightly, shrugging carelessly the shoulder he had held, 'I can always say I once knew a millionaire. How the girls back home are going to envy me when I boast of it! I might even tell them what you were like!'

'Tara!'

But she was at the door, his grim face behind her. She didn't turn to hear what he had been going to say next. Before he could draw breath, she said, 'I think I shall go to bed, Mr Voulgaris. I'm really tired.'

Minutes later she was in her cabin, a weight of misery pressing down on her, suffocating every sensible thought. Within her she felt a depression she had no idea how to get rid of, as she couldn't begin to guess the cause of it. When she ought to be rejoicing at the thought of seeing Tim and Veronica tomorrow, she could only feel despondent, but when a niggling voice at the back of her mind whispered that it had something to do with Damon Voulgaris she refused to believe it. She had called him Mr Voulgaris again and received a withering look in return. Yet she recalled him addressing her with a similar formality only a few minutes before she had left him, which seemed a clear indication that he was putting their relationship back on its proper footing. Maybe it was just as well they were returning to Polos tomorrow. Otherwise she might have let such attention as it had amused him to bestow on her go to her head.

Later she couldn't sleep, but it wasn't the fault of the yacht. The boat was quiet, silently ploughing its way through the dark waters of the Aegean. Switching on her light, Tara saw it was almost one o'clock and in the mirror she saw her haggard face. For a brief moment she also saw Damon Voulgaris, pale beneath his tan, as he had called her name, then his features faded. Restlessly she tried to assure herself. Tomorrow, or after tomorrow, she wouldn't be seeing him any more. If she did it would never be like this again. Certainly she wouldn't have to worry about him seeking her out. He would be only too keen to forget a girl who had proved to be little better than a nuisance!

On impulse she slipped out of bed and putting on her soft, easy to pack dressing gown, stole up on deck. There was no one about and the sudden desire to do something she might never get the opportunity of doing again came to her overwhelmingly. She wanted to stand against the rail, feel the night wind cool on her face, see the moon reflected in the mysterious darkness of the water and let the wild freedom of it all soothe her bruised spirit and bring her peace. When she sighed it was scarcely a breath to disturb the warm softness of the air.

No sound of footsteps came to her ear, but the voice which did seemed an intrusion. 'What do you think you are doing out here, Tara?'

Damon Voulgaris's impatience was a discordant note, just as she was feeling attuned to gentler things. Fleetingly she wondered why the natural sounds of the elements, no matter how fierce, never jarred like the sharp sound of a human voice. Storms might frighten, but they could also identify with something inside you.

Though startled she smiled, strangely reluctant to fight

with him on this last occasion. 'I couldn't sleep. I thought a breath of fresh air ...'

'A couple of aspirins would have solved your problem and been safer.'

'I'm sorry.' From his tone it would seem he didn't approve of her being here, but still she sought to placate him. 'I didn't think there would be any harm in coming on deck. It was only for a few moments.'

As she turned her head to look away from him, to take one last glance at the bewitching gleam of moonlight over the sea, the pureness of her profile was etched against the darkness, the elegance of her clear-cut features beautifully revealed as the slight wind blew her hair out behind her.

The man beside her went taut as his eyes fixed on her grimly. 'Girls who tantalise, as you do, play with fire. You light the fires, *thespinis*, yet cry when you get burnt. Or are you one of those who enjoy going up in flames? You leave your cabin——'

'Mr Voulgaris,' she interrupted his derisive flow, on a note of desperation, 'I thought you'd be in bed.'

'Didn't you think, even if I had been, some of my crew are always on duty?'

'But they don't happen to have designs on me!' she cried impatiently, as the peace around her dissolved rapidly before such an attack. 'None of them do more than say good morning, scarcely even that,' she added bitterly, 'if you're around.'

'Don't you realise?' he swept her protests harshly aside as his voice thickened. 'Don't you have the sense to understand you're a girl any man would desire?'

'Oh, really!'

Like a man driven almost beyond endurance, he grated furiously, 'I dislike insolence, girl! I try to be patient, but you refuse to listen. You will go to your cabin and stay there. And at once!'

Because he frightened her badly she felt she must defy

him. Her will against his might be like the flutterings of a small bird against the steel ribs of a cage, but for her pride's sake she must try. 'I've told you I'll go in a few minutes. I assure you I'm not in any danger—there's no need to be so fierce with me. Perhaps some of your crew might be kinder.'

Something inside him seemed to snap and, too late, she suspected she had gone too far. Even so she wasn't prepared for the cruelty of the arms which pulled her against him. The matching roughness in his voice as he spoke thickly in Greek against her cheek sent her head spinning, but when his mouth savagely took hers the very ocean seemed to heave and swirl under her feet, drawing her down into its dark, turbulent depths until she felt she was drowning.

CHAPTER FOUR

LATE the next afternoon, as she watched preparations going ahead for their departure from the yacht, Tara's head still ached. She had seen little of Damon all morning and he hadn't joined her for lunch. Georgios had said, when she had asked him if she shouldn't wait for Mr Voulgaris, that he and the captain had things to discuss.

Unhappily, Tara concluded, he wanted to avoid her, after last night. This she could understand as she felt a curious reluctance to exchange words with him herself. When she had struggled feverishly out of his arms, up here on the deck, in that midnight hour, strangely laced with enchantment, she had received the distinct impression that he was as disturbed as she, though perhaps in a different way. Anger had been the driving force behind Damon Voulgaris's violence, but her own reactions hadn't been so easy to explain.

When his arms had been around her, his mouth savagely on hers, she had felt fear, not so much of Damon as of herself, of the emotions he seemed able to arouse all too easily. Even without experience she had been aware that something was happening, of forces at work beyond her control. She might have thought beyond the control of either of them if she had dared, in that dizzying moment, to attempt to judge a man of Damon's character. As before, when he had kissed her, there was in her the same strange urgency to both cling to him and push him away. Later, she guessed it was the mounting passion in him which simultaneously excited and scared her. When, inevitably, he had pulled her closer she had struggled, but the ecstasy which began flooding her had been too overwhelming to fight. Her arms had gone tightly around his neck and, beneath his burning lips, she had huskily whispered his name. When, eventually, he had lifted his head she had found her own intense regret so alarming it had brought her back to her senses quicker than anything else might have done.

This time, when he released her, she hadn't known what to expect, but whatever it was she had thought he would utter it hadn't been an apology.

He had taken hold of her wrists to draw her arms from about his neck and put her firmly away from him. He had seemed fully in control of the situation, but the darkness of his eyes had lightened little as he had stared down on her pale face in the taut seconds which followed. 'I'm sorry,' he'd said, curtly. 'You provoked me, or I might have remembered you don't care for this sort of thing.'

'I don't—I mean, I didn't,' she faltered uncertainly, raising eyes unconsciously languorous from the force of her feelings. 'I think,' she whispered slowly, her head still partly among the stars, 'I'm getting used to it. It could be I'm even coming to like it.'

'Like it!' he had repeated, thick alarm in his voice as he met the soft glow in her eyes. 'Tara!' Then, pulling himself up with a jerk, just as she thought he was going to pull her to him again, he had stepped quickly back, his face regaining its familiar hardness. 'Don't let this little trip you're having go to your head, Tara. Of course you like it—the excitement, the novelty, perhaps, of travelling with a millionaire. Something, as you've already said, to boast of, to laugh over. Better to laugh at someone like me than to take him too seriously, my child.'

'I—I see.' A cloud had shadowed her face and she had been grateful it had hidden her sudden despair. By the time the wind had chased it gently away and the great golden moon again lit up her features, she had control of them. She had even managed a smile, bright enough to stop anyone imagining there had been a certain anguish in her eyes a moment ago. 'Please don't worry, Damon,' she had begged. 'I would be very stupid indeed if I were to let myself think you ever intended anything but a kind of punishment. I was foolish, annoying you at such an hour, and you chose your form of reprisal unthinkingly.'

'Punishment?' he had frowned, as he had taken an impatient step towards her. 'Tara!'

But Tara had fled, before he could say more, and she wondered if it would be the last time she would run from him, with the sound of her name on his lips. During their short journey together it seemed to have happened frequently.

Now she listened with dismay to the message Georgios brought. He came up to her, his tread soft. 'Excuse me, miss. Mr Voulgaris wishes to see you.'

'See me?' She had been gazing rather blindly towards Naxos, the beautiful Ionian island, the largest of the Cyclades, and she turned to stare at Georgios anxiously. 'Are you sure? I mean, we're just about to go ashore, aren't we?'

Georgios maintained a wooden stance. 'Mr Voulgaris would like you to go below, to his cabin, miss.'

'Oh, very well.' With a morose sigh but without further protest, she followed Georgios to the cabin door. To refuse such a request would probably be riskier than agreeing to it, though why Damon should want to see her like this she had no idea. Surely he didn't think it necessary to repeat the warnings he had given so contemptuously at midnight? Did he really consider her pride so low she would dream of making a nuisance of herself on Polos? Surely he didn't imagine she intended begging admittance to his villa on the strength of a few casual kisses?

'Come in,' she heard his deep voice commanding as Georgios knocked, then stood aside to allow her to pass. Behind her the door closed quietly and she found herself inside a cabin, a little larger than her own, and staring at the straight, proud line of Damon Voulgaris's broad back.

Unsure of what to expect, she hadn't thought to find him standing, staring rigidly out of the porthole. As she entered he turned and came over to where she stood uncertainly, just inside the door.

Tara tried to speak coolly, but the thought of saying anything at all was proving difficult. She got no comfort from reminding herself that she had only known this man for a few days and it was crazy to feel it could be more like a thousand years. Already he seemed so familiar she could scarcely bear to look at him. Asking him why he wanted to see her took a great deal more effort than she cared to think about.

The frown which began creasing his brow at the sight of her deepened, and Tara had the unbelievable impression that he was strangely at a loss for words. A movement passed while common sense assured her this could not be so. Damon Voulgaris would be master of every situation!

His eyes took in her trim cotton pants, the simple white top, under which her young body curved softly, and imperceptibly his glance darkened, as though he recalled too vividly what she had felt like in his arms. Then swiftly, his eyes hardening again, he said, 'I probably won't get another chance to speak to you, Tara, before we reach Polos. I just wanted to be sure you didn't think of me too badly because of this trip. There are one or two occasions I regret.'

Did he have to tell her so? Tara twisted around, pretending idle curiosity in her surroundings rather than that he should see her face grow white. Couldn't he have left it alone? Surely they had gone over this last night. He must certainly be cursing the fact that he had ever gone near her if he felt he must make doubly sure she understood his intentions had not been serious.

'Tara!' His voice was flat, so she could never guess from it exactly what he was thinking, but suddenly he was beside her. His hands came out, drawing her to him, whether with gentleness or checked impatience she couldn't tell, but his face dropped to rest momentarily against the side of her head. 'I would like to know you better, but I have some—business to attend to first and I'm not sure how long this is going to take. Until this is completed, I think it might be better if we remain just casual acquaintances. You understand?'

Unable to understand anything but a growing coldness, Tara lifted her chin, trying to hide the fact that she was trembling. Such a revulsion of feeling swept through her that she could scarcely bear to have him touch her. She had to keep a rigid hold of herself, so as not to cry out. Feverishly she whispered, 'You don't have to worry about me!'

His mouth tautened. 'But I do, Tara! I find you very sweet, with an honesty and innocence I can't help but admire, and I feel I must protect you from the force of my own feelings. You are very beautiful but so much younger than I am. You are not yet aware of the passion within you, a depth of response which might easily have betrayed you, had I carelessly insisted on making you mine. If, last night, I had carried you down here and laid you on my bed, could you have refused to let me love you? It is something you might have lived to regret, Tara, yet I find myself unable to explain. It is just that I believe something I have long wished for is, at last, coming my way and I don't want anything to spoil it.'

It must be a woman. Tara bit her lip unhappily, a feeling, too deep for tears, moving through her painfully. There must have been something in all the messages he had been receiving. Something from a woman—or about a woman—and he was making very sure that nothing got in the way. A brief, indiscreet dalliance with a girl he had been more or less forced to pick up would never be allowed to upset his serious plans for the future.

'I believe I understand now,' she said flatly, drawing herself bleakly from his arms. 'You can be quite sure you have nothing to fear from me.' A faint colour stole to her white cheeks. 'I think I could have resisted your midnight overtures better than you imagine, but, as you say, it's just as well that neither of us can have any real regrets.'

Far from appearing as relieved as she thought he would be, Damon Voulgaris frowned again, his glance probing Tara's sensitive face. 'Tara, you are sure of this?'

Firmly she clamped down on an hysterical desire to weep. That would be the final betrayal! This great brute of a man should never have the satisfaction of seeing her drowning in tears! She was beginning to think of the last few days, between leaving Athens and reaching Naxos, as a period designed to unnerve her. Once with Veronica and Tim she would be able to forget. Damon was probably right when he said that the glamour of a situation could distort the actual facts and give one entirely false ideas. She couldn't seem to bear her feelings as they were now, but once on Polos she would soon be looking back on this journey as a kind of fantasy, one which would fade from her mind in a very short time, as though it had never happened.

With an effort she spoke clearly. 'Of course I'm sure, I hope I have a little common sense,' Gaining confidence, she managed to smile into his frowning face. 'While there's the opportunity, Damon, I should like to thank you for being so kind to me. I really do appreciate that you've done your best to help me.'

'Thank you,' he said with irony, his glance slightly puzzled on her over-bright eyes. 'You've appreciated—everything?'

'Well——' Oh, damn him for pouncing like a tiger for the kill! Couldn't he stop playing with her? 'Almost everything,' she faltered, traces of strain now becoming quite visible, in her tear-thickened voice.

For a long moment he hesitated, his glance catching hers and holding it, until tension began whirling through her head in a dizzying spin. Then suddenly she was free as he left her on a rasping breath, and strode towards the door. 'I think we'd better go now, Tara. As things are between us, it might not be wise to linger. Otherwise we might never reach Polos today.'

The yacht anchored off the harbour while she and Damon were taken ashore. There was little time to note anything properly and Damon seemed preoccupied, almost to the extent of ignoring her. He did point out the small church of Anthony the Hermit, near the water's edge, which was built by the Knights of Rhodes who owned a commandery on the island. On an islet not far from the harbour, he added, could be seen the ruins of the temple of Dionysus, thought to have been built in the sixth century B.C.

On their way to his friend's house, where he had arranged that they should be picked up by helicopter, he mentioned that the island was famous for its marble, some of which had been used for the famous marble lions which they had seen on the holy island of Delos.

Before leaving the immediate vicinity of the harbour Tara allowed herself one last glimpse of the yacht, as it lay in resplendent whiteness in the jewel-like, blue-green sea. It seemed to represent something, she wasn't quite sure what, but she wasn't aware of how wistful her eyes were.

'You will see it again,' Damon quirked, although his eyes, as if trying to fathom her mood, were not as casual as his voice. 'Very soon it will lie at Polos.'

Holding her breath, Tara waited foolishly to hear him suggest she should go sailing with him again. When he merely frowned slightly and looked away, she realised hollowly that she had not been just imagining another woman.

The friend whose landing strip Damon was using was away, so there was nothing to prevent their immediate take-off. Never having flown in a helicopter before, she feared she was going to leave her stomach behind as the powerful rotor blades whirred into action above them and they rose abruptly into the air. Within seconds, however, as the pilot expertly controlled the great machine and they levelled out, she felt better and was able to appreciate the wonderful view beneath them. Then the beautiful valleys and mountains were gone and they were over the sea again, their reflection painted so vividly on the water that, for a moment, she felt they were falling and clutched Damon's arm nervously.

The pilot grinned apologetically, while Damon smiled and told her not to worry. Quickly Tara removed her hand, annoyed with herself for panicking, letting the silky fall of her hair hide the embarrassed pink in her cheeks.

Though the incident passed and she composed herself, it disturbed other thoughts which she had, for days, pushed to the back of her mind. Unable to stop herself, she turned to Damon. 'Do you think Tim and Veronica will really be pleased to see me?' Suddenly her eyes were wide and rather frightened, like those of a child.

Damon frowned as his glance took in her unconscious apprehension. 'You seem too anxious. When did you last see your brother?'

'I haven't seen him for over six years.'

'Good God, child, aren't your parents throwing you in at the deep end! Neither your brother or his wife ...' He paused, a thin line of anger to his mouth, but whatever else he had been going to say he obviously changed his mind.

Tara didn't notice. 'You keep calling me a child,' she protested, 'but soon I shall be twenty-two. A lot of girls have been earning their living for years before this age.'

Startling her, his hand went over hers, as if he must

have the touch of her, and the message conveyed silently through his dark eyes made her suddenly tremble. 'I am quite aware of this, Tara. In most cases this renders a young woman very capable of looking after herself, but I don't think I am speaking to a girl who has been as yet exposed to the necessity of earning her own living. You haven't been out in the world long enough to grow a protective skin.'

Because she liked the feel of his caressing fingers and the feeling of being curiously alone with him, in spite of the presence of the pilot, she didn't do anything to stop herself burning a little in his smouldering gaze. He appeared to have taken her under his wing and she had grown to like him, perhaps more than was sensible, but there was little fight left in her to ponder on the wisdom of this in that dazzling moment of brilliant sunshine. A light was illuminating her heart with the same bright intensity, although she wasn't aware of the actual cause of it. It was good, she was discovering, to feel protected, even by this man who, more than likely, belonged to another woman. The warmth within her spread, dispersing the momentary coldness aroused by the shadow of this other woman, along with all her former desire for complete independence. With Damon Voulgaris so near and holding her hand so closely, all thought of being independent was fading rapidly.

But even while acknowledging to herself that she felt happier for Damon's kindness, Tara knew she mustn't allow herself to be carried away by it. People in distress might always move him, there need be nothing personal about his silent gesture of comfort. He had seemed oddly censorious of Tim and Veronica, though, and she felt she should make some protest. There was such a thing as family loyalty! 'Is there any reason,' she asked faintly, 'why you feel I'm about to be thrown to the wolves?'

'Come,' he smiled mockingly, 'I hope I didn't give such a bad impression as all that. Your brother has been rather unpredictable lately, and your sister-in-law a little discontent, but we all are subject to moods.'

How did Damon know this? His words were casual but, even so, only those who were well acquainted with someone could know this of them. Damon had never intimated that he was on such close terms with Tim and his wife. Uncertainly she glanced at him, but something in his expression warned that he would not be willing to answer any more questions, not on this subject. Maybe he had had about enough of both her and her family and the small flaws he would find in people, others might never notice. It would take a very superior being to live up to Damon Voulgaris's high expectations, she decided ruefully.

It was dark when they reached Polos, which seemed to be an island more isolated than most. Dark, with the moon not yet risen, and fleetingly, Tara wondered if Damon had deliberately planned it as she could see very little of his villa though they landed beside it. The pilot took straight off again and Damon, after a brief word to a hovering manservant, put Tara and her suitcases immediately into a waiting car.

'I will take you to your brother's taverna myself,' he informed a slightly bewildered Tara courteously, getting in beside her and slamming the door.

'If you like,' she said hastily, and unthinkingly, 'I could wait at your villa until Tim arrives. If you would be kind enough to give him a ring and tell him I'm here?'

His dark eyes narrowing, Damon glanced at her as he switched the ignition. 'Haven't I already said I will take you, Miss Curtis? It is only a matter of a few miles. It will be easier and quicker, in the long run, if I deliver you myself.'

'Yes, of course.' She was instantly mortified at his cold tone. He sounded almost suspicious, wearily so, although the exact source of this impression eluded her. Unless— she bent her fair head over her hands as they started off— unless it was because of Greg Golden? If he actually was here, naturally Damon wouldn't want her seeing him! He wouldn't want her anywhere near his villa!

On the way to the small village, where the taverna lay, Tara was silent. The countryside around them was dark and quiet. It ought to have been soothing, but the feeling of unity she had shared with Damon in the helicopter had gone and she felt terribly on edge.

It was only as they neared the flickering lights, which suggested they were approaching some kind of community, that she spoke. And it was so impulsively she immediately regretted it and would have done anything to have been able to have taken it back.

'I'm sorry, Damon, to have dragged you all the way here. You probably have guests whom you wish to see as soon as possible . . .'

'What—guests?'

'Oh, I'm sorry,' too late, Tara realised her mistake and stumbled to correct it, 'I didn't mean to pry. When you said you had to return to Polos urgently, I simply concluded . . .'

'I never said anything about anything being urgent.' His voice, cold and wary, made his statement indisputable. 'You jump to too many conclusions, Miss Curtis. I should advise you in future to stop conjecturing about all and sundry and consequently becoming a positive source of irritation!'

Something in his tone stung Tara out of her growing apathy—this, and the way he had reverted to addressing her formally. The first time she had thought it must have been accidental, but now she was convinced he was trying to make it very clear that any casual intimacy between them was over. Pride sharpened her voice as she exclaimed bitterly, 'If you did have guests I don't suppose you'd want them to know someone like me.'

'We have arrived at the home of your brother, *thespinis*.' Savagely Damon swung the car from the indifferent road on which they had been travelling, into a village street.

A long street of white houses which gleamed ghost-like through the darkness and, apart from the odd dog and tethered donkey, appeared deserted. A little further on, his driving still dictated by a touch of violence, he ground to a halt before a low, two-storied building by the sea.

'I will see you safely inside.'

His abrupt politeness made Tara shiver. His face was hard, she noticed, the jerk of his head arrogant, and he hadn't even bothered to answer her question. 'It doesn't matter.' She swallowed dismally, yet was suddenly terrified of going into the taverna alone. 'If I can just get my cases.'

'Ah, yes,' for a second he showed faint amusement, 'I seem to have been lugging them halfway around the world. Perhaps your brother should take a turn.' Firmly he depressed his fingers on the horn, not once but several times.

The subsequent noise seemed alarming. 'Please stop!' Tara cried.

A moment later he obliged, but the glance he threw at her nervous face was impatient. 'We are not so reluctant to make ourselves heard in this part of the world, my dear, but, *mon dieu*, it would indeed take an earthquake to get some service around here!'

After expressing himself in French, in no uncertain terms, Voulgaris picked up her two suitcases and strode towards the door, Tara stumbling hastily after him. She wondered despairingly how many more times she would be forced to follow him like this. It seemed to be becoming almost a regular occurrence!

He shouldered open the door, which looked as if it could do with a new coat of paint, and dropped her luggage just inside, as though he couldn't wait to be rid of it. The hall was narrow with a rather makeshift reception desk crammed into one side of it, along with a few slightly drunken-looking chairs, supported by a drably decorated wall. Altogether it was vaguely depressing, but Tara felt too relieved to have got here to let it worry her unduly.

'Wait here.' As if wholly familiar with the place, Voulgaris left her abruptly, to disappear through another door, leaving Tara to continue her wide-eyed inspection. Minutes later he was back with Tim and a dark, curly-headed woman tagging along behind him. He looked on enigmatically but curiously watchful as Tim welcomed her.

'Infant!' Tim's smile appeared a trifle weary, but it was kind, and he held his arms wide for Tara to run into them, as she had done so many times as a baby when Tim had often been the one to pick her up. After hugging her lightly, he released her, laughing as his eyes went quickly over her. After emanating a low wolf whistle, he laughed teasingly. 'Not so much of the infant now, is it? You've certainly grown some since I last saw you, but I guess that was only to be expected. You've grown prettier, too.' His smile faded and suddenly he frowned. Then, obviously collecting himself, he said brightly, 'Come and meet your sister-in-law, Tara. It seems really crazy that you two don't yet know each other!'

Turning to Veronica uncertainly, Tara held out her hand. Tim's wife took it limply while eyeing Tara doubtfully. 'You're not much like Tim,' she said.

'Well,' Tara moistened her lips as the quick animosity in Veronica's eyes made them dry, 'I believe,' she heard herself saying, rather inanely, 'I take after my mother.'

'Of course she does,' Tim threw his wife a cynical glance. 'You wouldn't want her to look like me, would you?' He glanced at Damon, opened his mouth as if to speak to him, then closed it again, as though something about the way Voulgaris was watching his sister puzzled him. He tried another approach. 'Good of you to bring her, Damon.'

'I hope she wasn't too much of a nuisance,' Veronica added, giving Damon a brilliant smile.

Damon's mouth twitched, but he replied very soberly,

his eyes leaving Veronica's beguiling ones to return to Tara's pink face. 'Not what you could really call a nuisance.'

Veronica laughed, rather brittlely. 'What a wasted opportunity! How many of us would have loved to have been in your shoes, Tara.'

Tim grimaced, but didn't seem at all put out by the languishing glances his wife was casting at the big Greek millionaire. 'Joking aside, Damon, I'm glad she was able to travel in comfort. She might never get chance to enjoy such style again.'

There were undercurrents here which Tara didn't understand. She felt bewildered, not caring for the way in which they all seemed to be talking as though she wasn't there. Even Damon was regarding her with amusement. 'I've already thanked Mr Voulgaris,' she said stiffly, 'and told him how much I've appreciated his help.'

Into the sudden silence came a roar of loud laughter from the room behind them. Voulgaris frowned. 'Busy?' he asked Veronica, staring at her coldly.

'You could say,' she replied flippantly, shrugging her shoulders without removing her eyes from his face. She was so obviously absorbed by him, her young sister-in-law might never have existed.

Tim, flashing Tara a brief smile, asked Damon quickly, 'Can I get you a drink?'

'No, thank you, I want to get back.' He turned away from Veronica to stare at Tara again. Moving closer, he looked narrowly down on her uncertain face. 'You'll be all right?'

'Yes.' There was no need to betray her regret that he was leaving. Veronica was surely expressing more than enough adulation! Tara kept her own eyes firmly fixed on the top button of his shirt. 'Thank you again, Mr Voulgaris. You've been very kind.'

She missed the way his face darkened. There was only

the light touch of his hand on her shoulder, then he was gone, with the roar of his sharply wakened engine protesting in the quiet air outside. Tara shivered, having the strangest feeling that something important had gone from her life—without being able to understand exactly what.

Veronica said quickly, as if not caring for the sudden silence which fell after Damon's departure, 'You'd better go and quieten them down a little in there, Tim. I'll stay and get acquainted with your sister.'

As Tim disappeared with a sigh and a 'see you,' Veronica took Tara into a small private sitting room at the other end of the hall. 'When Tim comes back,' she promised, 'I'll ask him to try and find you something to eat. The girls shouldn't be long in finishing in the kitchen, but they're very slow. We have a devil of a job with labour. Most of those available work at other things or in the large hotels on the other islands. Tim and I don't stand a chance. Even Damon can get a better supply of housemaids than we can.' She hesitated only fractionally before rushing on, 'Tell me about your trip, Tara. I can't wait to hear everything.'

Tara blinked, feeling rather dazed, as Veronica flung herself down on a small settee, leaving her standing. Nervously Tara found herself wondering if this was the kind of treatment she might expect during her visit. Even Damon had been kinder than this. Yet recalling his flash of anger, when she had thanked him for it, she felt puzzled and transferred her attention to Veronica again.

Thinking she might well remain standing if she didn't look after herself, she seated herself opposite and asked politely and, with what she hoped was a warm smile, 'The plane wasn't crowded ...'

'Not the plane, silly!' Veronica reached for a cigarette, glancing at Tara impatiently. 'Damon's yacht! I want to hear all about it. Was there anyone else there? Another woman, I mean?'

'Why, no.' Tara stared at her in astonishment. What

sort of relationship did Tim and his wife have if she could be so interested in another man? Maybe it was wrong to expect Veronica to be interested in in-laws who had practically ignored her existence for years. Not that all the blame could be placed on Tim's family as they had really had no idea of Tim's marriage until he had sent word from out here. Perhaps the lack of sympathy between Tim and his parents was basically at fault, but surely Veronica must want to help a little towards putting things right? 'No,' Tara thought it might be a good idea to humour Veronica, to start with, anyway, 'there was no one.'

Veronica drew deeply on her cigarette, considering this for a moment. 'You fell for him, of course. All women do, regardless of their age. He's a very attractive man as well as being a very rich one.'

'Veronica, please!' Her pulse racing, Tara felt she must put a stop to this before it went any further. 'Mr Voulgaris might be everything you say, but I did *not* fall for him!'

'It's like shock,' Veronica continued as if Tara had never spoken, her eyes dreamy. 'It doesn't hit you until afterwards.'

Tara wasn't sure Veronica wasn't right, but she was sure she wouldn't openly agree with her. Somehow a halt must be called to such nonsense. 'To me, Mr Voulgaris was just a man who was being helpful. I don't think we had much in common and I didn't see a lot of him.'

'And there's certainly plenty of him to see!' Veronica's sigh was wistful, yet happier. 'I didn't really think, from what Tim told me, you would be his type, but when he sent word that it might be a week or two before you got here—well, I was naturally anxious.'

'A week or two?' As Tara drew off her light jacket and laid it carefully over her knees, she blinked in bewilderment. 'Oh, I'm sure you're wrong. I believe it was only going to be for a few days, and this was because something cropped up and he had people to see. Unfortunately, he had to come back here before he could see anyone. I don't know why, so it's no use asking!'

'I expect because his stepbrother and his fiancée are here.' Veronica looked thoughtful. 'We often don't hear of half the people who arrive, if they fly in by helicopter or a small plane, but whoever's here now must be important to bring Damon running.'

'He said it wasn't urgent, actually.'

Veronica frowned, taking another deep drag of her cigarette, then resentfully contemplating the end of it. 'That's the worst of Damon! One can never discover what's important to him. He seems to take a positive pleasure in keeping one guessing!'

'Do you see much of him when he visits the island?' Tara hadn't meant to ask. She certainly didn't wish to give the impression she was as eager to discuss him as Veronica! Yet, she hastened to assure herself, to ask a few questions might arouse Veronica's suspicious less than if she asked none.

'It depends,' Veronica was saying. 'Sometimes we see him often, but if he's entertaining special guests then he isn't here so much. Usually Tim and I get an invitation to dinner.'

'I don't suppose he ever has a great deal of time to spend on the island?' Tara hoped she sounded sensible. 'I mean, with his business and all that.'

'I think his business almost runs itself now, and he only employs the best.'

'But it must be the money he makes from it,' Tara insisted, 'which makes him so fascinating to a lot of women.' Perhaps this would make Veronica realise just what a snare wealth could be! That the wealth of a man like Damon Voulgaris could be blinding her to Tim's superior qualities.

Veronica stretched, like a sleek cat, her over-abundance of curves very obvious. Slowly she smiled, her eyes on

Tara's anxious young face. 'But, apart from his money, darling, Damon's extremely compelling. A girl has the excitement of never knowing where she is with him. He's no weakling to be ordered around at will. His very personality is unusual! One moment he's as rigidly Greek as you would find, the next, just as completely English. They say he speaks about half a dozen languages fluently, but I believe he always resorts to Greek when something moves him.'

'I see ...'

'And his villa is quite something—you should see it! In fact, I'll try to wangle you an invitation if he asks Tim and me to dine before he goes away again. Mind you, I've heard some talk of his selling, but I'm sure it won't be in the near future.'

'He isn't married.' Now Tara was feeling so uptight she was just saying the first thing to enter her head. Veronica's whole attitude regarding Damon Voulgaris was startling.

'This is what's really difficult to understand.' Veronica sounded smug. 'Sometimes, I think, that in spite of all the beautiful women he meets, he must have a secret yearning for someone unobtainable. A married woman, perhaps?'

Alarmed, Tara stared at her sister-in-law, noting her fanciful expression. Surely she couldn't mean herself? Veronica was Tim's age. She would still be younger than Damon Voulgaris, of course, and for all she was well built was very attractive. The petulant droop to her mouth didn't improve her, nor did the discontent in her eyes, but otherwise, with her thick dark hair and even features, she was very nice-looking.

'I think you have too much imagination,' Tara tried to laugh lightly. 'Whether she were married or not, I have the impression that if Damon Voulgaris wanted a woman he wouldn't allow that to stand in his way! Not in the end.'

'Just what I've been thinking!' Veronica dismayed

Tara by exclaiming triumphantly. She gazed at Tara with a smile which was at last full of approbation. With a sleek stretch of satisfaction she rose. 'If you like,' she suggested exactly as if Tara was some unknown summer visitor, 'I can show you to your room. I'm afraid it's not very big.'

It wasn't until later, as she was getting into bed, that Tara recalled what Veronica had said about Damon's stepbrother staying at the villa. With a curious hurt in her heart she wondered why, when she had talked so much about Tim, he had never mentioned having a brother, too. It hurt even more to realise that this must have been the reason he had hurried her away. Obviously Damon hadn't wanted them to meet!

CHAPTER FIVE

NOT very big was scarcely the right description, Tara decided ruefully next morning as she dressed before running downstairs. There was barely room to swing a cat! However, what did a room matter in such wonderful surroundings—she wouldn't be spending much time in it. Through her window warm sunshine beckoned, even at this early hour, and when she ran over to it, she could see through the clear glass the vivid blue of the sea and what looked like miles of white sands. Faced with such a delightful prospect the strangeness of Veronica's conversation the evening before wore off a little.

Last night Veronica had shown her to her room, then left her, after thanking her quite sweetly for agreeing to come and work for them. After she had gone Tara couldn't really put her finger on anything she could criticise, yet nothing about her new-found sister-in-law seemed very satisfactory. Something was wrong, Tara felt sure, but she was also equally sure that Veronica's discontent lay not with her so much as Tim. Uneasily she wondered if Damon Voulgaris was involved. Veronica had seemed very interested in him, and she didn't doubt that Voulgaris would have no scruples about Veronica being married if he were interested in her.

With a sigh, Tara strove to put this thought from her, not sure why it should hurt. Last night, after Veronica had left her, after declaring she was tired and going off to bed, Tara had felt too restless—and hungry—to do the same. After washing her face and hands she had wandered downstairs again to the sitting room. Tim had eventually reappeared with two mugs of coffee and a plate of sandwiches. When she had explained why Veronica wasn't there, he had sat down and helped her eat the refreshments himself. They had talked a long time, chiefly about their father's illness and their mother's practice. Jonathan had scarcely been mentioned and Tara hadn't said anything about what he expected her to do for him.

As she had got up to go back to her room, Tim had asked, a little abstractedly, if she would like to get up to help with breakfast. She had agreed and, this morning, she found him in the kitchen, all on his own.

'Good morning,' she smiled at him rather shyly, because the years seemed to have driven a chasm between them which wasn't yet bridged. Since she had last seen him she had grown up and she suspected he wasn't quite sure how to treat her.

'Is Veronica up?' she enquired lightly, after Tim had returned her greeting.

'No, not yet.' Tim glanced at her uncomfortably. 'She's feeling awfully tired this morning, Tara, and wondered if you would mind if she stayed in bed for an extra hour. It's understandable, of course,' he hurried on, 'all those summer visitors.'

Tara said she didn't mind a bit. She didn't add that she would be glad of the breathing space because there was no reason why she should feel that way and it would only offend Tim. She spoke soothingly as he looked anxious. 'It's quite all right, Tim, I understand. I suppose it's only in the depth of winter you can really take things easy?'

'Sometimes not even then,' he shrugged. 'We don't have people coming all the year round, but during the slack periods I try to catch up on the work in the boat yard. Right now I'm a hell of a way behind and ...' Whatever he had been going to say he apparently changed his mind. His mouth clamped, his frown deepened as he went on grinding coffee.

'Oh, yes, your boat-building business.' To think of it only aroused more disappointment at not being able to go outside, so she turned her thoughts elsewhere. 'Shall I take

Veronica a cup of tea or coffee—and, about breakfast, do you have anyone staying at the moment? That is,' she smiled, 'apart from me?'

'Veronica's already had something,' Tim grimaced wryly. 'As for people staying, we have three German couples and a Frenchman. The French chap is doing some kind of research on the islands, prior to writing a book. They're all charming and very friendly, but they also have damned good appetites!'

Tara looked at him rather helplessly. 'Don't you just give them so much?'

'Good heavens, no, child. That would be no good at all for business. There's nothing much else to do here but sleep and eat. It's only by giving people as much food and drink as they want that they come back.'

'Tim,' she frowned, not quite knowing what to make of it, the way he looked both resigned and half desperate at the same time, 'haven't you ever considered coming back to England?'

'No!' He laughed suddenly, as if determined to throw off his black mood. 'I'm much better here, so don't try to persuade me. Once I get the boatyard really going I might be able to persuade Veronica to give up this side of the business.'

It was funny, Tara thought, over two hours later as she began washing up, how things very rarely turned out the way you expected. Breakfast was just over, yet already she was beginning to feel exhausted. It must be those lotus-eater days on Damon's yacht which were responsible for this alarming weakness. She would certainly have to toughen up if she was to survive here!

Tim had stayed and helped, but he had also instructed her so carefully on how to cook for numbers that she had the horrible suspicion that it was to become her regular task. The paying guests, with obviously the sole object in mind of getting their money's worth, had eaten such quantities of food as to leave Tara almost gasping. As Tim had said, they were charming, but very demanding!

She had learnt from Tim, while they had served breakfast, that two girls usually came and helped with dinner, and an old, retired but very good chef, who lived in the village, could be persuaded to turn out when he needed a little extra money. Otherwise there was no one and it was very clear he expected Tara to make herself useful, although there was no mention of any salary.

Veronica stayed upstairs until lunch time, while Tara flew around, trying to do what she considered the more important jobs first. Tim helped, continuing his pre-breakfast method of instruction, until Tara soon had a good general idea of how to go on.

Over coffee Tim remarked with some satisfaction, 'There's still the marketing and the bar, things like that, but if you could manage the cooking and housework I'm sure Veronica could do the rest. It will be great to get back to my boatbuilding!'

Taking a quick sip of her coffee, Tara said hesitantly, 'I won't be staying for ever, you know. I would like to get properly acquainted with Veronica and stay with you a few weeks, but I have to think of my future, of a career.'

'Well, see how things work out.' Tim didn't seem to take this at all seriously as he glanced indifferently at Tara's anxious face. 'You look as though you could do with a few months out here, and once you get used to the work, you'll be able to get through it quite quickly and have plenty of time left each day to relax. Veronica too could do with a break, you know. Get proficient enough and I might even take her off for a long holiday and leave you in charge.' He jumped to his feet, clapping her lightly, with brotherly exuberance, on her aching back. 'How would that be for quick promotion!'

Tara kept telling herself she wouldn't really have minded being taken so completely for granted if either Tim or Veronica had shown a little genuine appreciation. During the next days she noticed how they both seemed absorbed, not in each other, but in themselves. It was only natural that they had their own particular problems, but while Jonathan and his wife went in for sharing and togetherness, Tim and Veronica seemed to have no real patience with each other, although they never discussed each other with Tara. This, she decided, must be a good indication that they still, at least, had some loyalty left.

Veronica spent most of her time in the bar, laughing with the German couples, or sunning herself on the beach with the Frenchman. The Frenchman must obviously be researching a little romance along with everything else, Tara thought dryly, as he was never far from Veronica's side and had even asked Tara to go for a stroll in the moonlight with him twice. Tim was away for hours at his boatyard and didn't, after the first day, take much notice of his sister. Only once, when he had looked particularly down, had she brought up the subject of England again.

He had merely laughed and shaken his head. 'This is my home now, infant. I rarely think of the old U.K. any more.'

'But Mum and Daddy?'

'God, baby! I've outgrown you all, years ago.'

'But Mum said—we all thought you were hurt when you quarrelled with Daddy?'

'All sons quarrel with Daddy,' he mimicked mockingly. 'That was certainly not why I left home. Maybe I used it as an excuse.'

'Mum said you were hurt!'

'Tara!' Tim had thrown up his hands in protest. 'Mothers always believe their sons are being hurt, feeling hurt. It's a universal affliction. One of these days, if they don't come over here, I'll take Veronica to see them, but I'm not breaking my heart!' With an impatient sigh he had left.

'By the way,' Veronica said, a few minutes later, as though Tim's indifference hadn't disturbed Tara enough, 'I forgot to tell you, but while you were still on your way,

Jonathan rang. He seemed very anxious about you, but absolutely refused to confide in me, darling. He did say you would know why he was so keen to get in touch with you. He's the journalist, isn't he?'

Tara felt her face pale. 'I expect he was only ringing to find out if I'd arrived safely . . .'

'Uh-huh!' Veronica stared at her sharply. 'Well, he's rung twice. Again when you were along the beach, last night, and if that's not wonderful brotherly love, I'll eat my hat!'

Veronica's voice was so sarcastic, Tara felt herself going bright red.

At this Veronica's eyes narrowed. 'You haven't promised him an article on a Greek taverna, or perhaps the boatyard, have you, Tara? If so, I can tell you right now, Tim wouldn't like it.'

'Of course not.' That, at least, was the truth. 'We don't see much of him. Like Tim, we rarely hear from him unless he wants something.'

Cat-like, Veronica smiled. 'It gets even more interesting as you go on, but I'm afraid I hear someone in the bar.'

Blessing her careless tongue, Tara continued with the task in hand. She really must take more care in future, and she must tell Jonathan to stop ringing! Hadn't she promised to drop him a note, if she discovered anything? Damon hadn't been here for three days, not since he had brought her here, but if he heard of this he would no doubt be making hot tracks for the door. Her heart thudded at the thought of seeing him again, but she quickly dismissed the hard, masculine image of him from her head. This wasn't a boat, where his every movement might be noted. If she angered him, on what was virtually his own island, heaven knows what he might do to her!

She was behind the bar the next evening when Damon arrived. Veronica had asked her to take over while she had her evening meal. Tim had only just got in and was upstairs having a shower. Two of the Germans were laughing uproariously at the mistakes she was making and exchanging loud jokes in German which she didn't understand. While she felt she ought to be joining in their uninhibited merriment the most she could manage was a slightly nervous smile.

One of the men, when she turned to reach for a certain bottle, leant over the narrow counter and gave her bottom a suggestive slap. '*Liebling*,' he chortled, 'I'd rather have you than the best cognac. Even the rarest hock we could find on the Rhine would be no sweeter than you.'

'Good evening, Tara!'

Tara gasped, a fright of a different kind overtaking her as she heard Damon's voice and the grim disapproval in it burnt her ears. Slowly she turned and she saw at once he was furious. For some reason his face was pale, his mouth tight and when he spoke again he sounded even grimmer. 'Run and get your coat while I find someone to take over here.'

The other men were looking at him curiously, but he took no notice as he strode quickly towards the kitchen. Tara knew she should tell him he wouldn't find Veronica or Tim there, but her voice wouldn't seem to function.

Whatever he did in the kitchen he was some minutes in coming out. 'Where is your sister-in-law?' he asked curtly.

'In the—the small sitting room.'

'Veronica!' she heard him exclaim sharply as he closed the door behind him.

Seconds later he was back with a flushed but otherwise composed Veronica by his side. Obviously not going to betray her anger before guests, she spoke to Tara shortly. 'I'll manage now. I believe Damon wants a word with you.'

'More than a word.' Damon's eyes glinted. 'Get your coat, Tara, or I'll do it for you.'

Quickly, an odd fear leaping in her heart, she obeyed. After three days of almost non-stop work she was almost too tired to protest. She ran upstairs and sought a light jacket as she hadn't brought a coat. The night was warm enough, though, and she wouldn't be long, in spite of Damon threatening otherwise. Feeling slightly reassured, she went down again, but was unhappily conscious of Veronica's vindictive glance as she went out.

Once away from the taverna she stopped, tugging on the arm Damon was using to drag her along. They were on the beach, making towards a small cove, unadorned apart from a few sparse trees. At any hour of the day, at this time of the year it might be deserted, but to Tara, at that moment, it might have been the loneliest place on earth.

'Mr Voulgaris!' she cried.

'Damon!' he exploded tersely.

'I don't like your tone!' she retorted.

'There's a hell of a lot more you aren't going to like, so I'd advise you to wait before you express yourself too freely!' Ruthlessly he took no notice of her feeble, delaying tactics. The scarcely controlled impatience in his long, supple stride carried her with him at such speed she tripped and was consequently half hauled for several yards until her choking cries of protest brought him to a reluctant halt.

With hands which were far from gentle he drew her closer, disregarding quite carelessly the blind fury in her face. 'How long have you been behind that bar?' he flung at her, his anger more than matching her own. 'Answer me, my girl,' he commanded coldly, as she stared at him silently, with wide, dilated eyes.

'Really, Mr—I mean, Damon,' she stuttered helplessly, 'I don't see that it's any of your business!'

'Say that once again,' he cut in, 'and you'll be sorry for the rest of your life!'

All of a sudden her temper left her and without its invisible support she trembled, as other less stiffening emotions rushed in. Tears stung her eyes and she blinked them back quickly because the moonlight was bright enough for him to see. 'I don't know how you can stand there and say such things,' she faltered, trying to ignore the blaze of fire which went through her as his hands bit into her shoulders. 'You haven't been near me since you brought me back!' she said loudly, thinking, belatedly, that a little aggression might hide the real state of her feelings.

He laughed, but his laughter was no kinder than his words. 'Did you expect me to come running like a pet cur, my girl?'

'You're insolent!'

'By heavens ... !'

As she literally shook with nerves she realised, intuitively, that no one had ever spoken to him like this. His face held a soul-shaking anger. 'Damon! I'm sorry ...' All her bravado collapsed as she wished miserably she had never spoken as she had. 'I'm sorry,' she whispered again when he made no reply, 'I—we have been busy and I think I must be tired.'

For endless seconds as he towered over her she thought his anger was going to win, then suddenly he appeared to change. The tension in his hands relaxed and he sighed. 'Sparks, Tara,' he exclaimed. 'Why do sparks fly between us each time we meet? Are you not aware of this?'

Silently she continued to stare at him, so busy wondering why this should be that she forgot to so much as nod her head. 'You get so angry with me, Damon.'

A little of his anger returned and she wished she hadn't mentioned it. 'My God, it was enough to make any man furious to find you behind that bar and hear another man calling you darling! He was being too familiar, and instead of repulsing him you chose to display your attractions most blatantly.'

'That's not true!' she gasped. 'I had my back to him.'

'So? You have very nice curves, *liebling*!' mockingly he mimicked the German, 'both back and front!'

Her cheeks grew hot and she cried defensively, 'Those

men are really very nice. They just enjoy teasing me a little.'

'I have no doubt. *Thespinis,* that man is married and old enough to be your father.'

Thinking to improve matters, she rejoined, 'He was only being playful.'

'So you enjoy the man who is playful, *thespinis*? You won't object if I lift my hand—thus?'

She gave a small, startled cry as he raised a hand which was far from playful, bringing it down with a sharp slap which actually hurt. 'Damon—please!'

'Please—what?' His voice was as sharp as his hand and just as disapproving.

Feeling her nerves strung so tight she could hardly contain them, she said dejectedly, 'Don't you start making fun of me!'

Repressively his mouth tightened as he met her wide, defensive eyes in the moonlight. His hand went out to tilt her chin, as though he would see her reactions even more clearly. 'With me you shriek and look angry, but with those others you laugh!'

'Yes. But,' she protested, with a suddenly wry smile, 'he didn't hurt.'

'If I did, it wasn't as much as you deserved. I feel you ought to be punished. You should learn to work without making such a display of your body.'

'Damon!' A fiery heat was in her cheeks, but when she tried to struggle from him she failed. How dared he speak to her like this? 'Will you please stop! I don't want to hear any more of your insults!' With her hands she tried to push him away, only to find herself caught against the hard warmth of his chest as he pulled her closer to him.

'I still feel the need to punish you, Tara, and I believe actions often impress more than mere words.'

As he bent his head she tried again to escape him, but

because of his strength, she found it impossible. The hand which was already curving her tender jaw forced her face up, and swiftly, so she scarcely knew what was happening, his lips found hers. On the moment of impact she was conscious of a deep, quivering sigh which seemed to shatter any desire she had had to reject him. His arms left her shoulders to wrap around her slight body as if he, too, felt the nervous quiver and it afforded him some satisfaction. His anger not yet appeased, he crushed her mouth roughly under his until, along with the sensuous rapture, she was conscious of pain. She moaned faintly, but if he heard he paid no attention. He was kissing her as though he had been thinking of nothing else for three whole days, as though he couldn't get enough of the ardent feel of the vulnerable young mouth so helplessly at his mercy.

When at last he called a halt all the fight had gone out of her. She could only watch, bemused, as he twisted a heavy strand of hair behind her ear and bent to put his lips to it. As his mouth pursued the pale curve of her neck, began exploring the soft hollow at the base of her throat, she felt her limbs grow weak.

Then, his eyes watchful, he put her gently away from him, turning her back to his side to follow the flickering track of moonlight across the beach. The tide raced, bringing the dark, glinting waves almost to their feet, hinting at a turbulence which Tara thought might well match her own. There was nothing in the casualness of the arm Damon placed around her shoulders, however, to suggest he felt the same inner sense of disturbance.

'Come,' he said coolly. 'It is more private further on and we have still to discuss that which I came to talk about in the first place. You are too distracting, Tara. We appear to strike sparks off each other, and each time we meet, I must convince myself it is only in my imagination. I did not intend kissing you, but there seems always a desire to punish.'

So it had been—unintentional, a kind of natural extension of his anger. With words she could answer back, but against his superb physical strength she had no hope of fighting with any degree of success. 'Anger often drives people to act as they wouldn't do normally,' she uttered primly.

She thought she saw his mouth quirk briefly, as if he found what she said ironically amusing, but he didn't openly contradict her. Almost as if he guessed her thoughts his arm tightened, so she could not turn and flee as she suddenly wanted to.

Further on was a cove guarded by tall trees and, under the shadow of these, against a sandy rise he released her, bidding her to sit down. As she reluctantly obeyed, he placed himself near enough to prevent any impulsive desire to escape. 'Now tell me,' he demanded curtly, 'why you have spent all your time slaving at the taverna since you arrived?'

It would be foolish to lie, this she realised. Damon was too astute, but she didn't want to be guilty of disloyalty. While she hesitated he came nearer, tilting up her chin, as seemed to be becoming a habit of his.

'The truth!' he insisted.

Because he spoke so emphatically she could see no way of avoiding it. Unhappily she confessed, 'Tim was behind with his work. He wanted to catch up.'

'What—work?'

'His boatyard. I haven't seen it yet, but he did tell me how important it is. It's also doing well, or would be if he could give it some proper attention.'

'So he decided, before his young sister almost had time to draw breath, that she should take over his household tasks so he could get on with it?'

'Yes.' Tara was relieved that Damon immediately understood the situation and didn't seem unduly disturbed. 'Once Tim has caught up, I expect ...'

'What do you expect?' he prompted, with deceptive smoothness as she paused.

Tara, unsure as to why Damon's quiet tones should belatedly be arousing her suspicions, continued more uncertainly, 'Well, I just thought, when this happens, I'd have more free time.'

'But if he allows you any, won't his boatyard begin to suffer again?'

'I'm not sure. Yes—I suppose so . . .'

'You suppose so!' Suddenly, so savagely he took her by surprise, he turned her to face him. 'Don't you know, you little fool, Tim lost interest in the taverna long ago? Just as long as you're willing to stay there you'll be made to work, unless you assert yourself. Was it arranged that you should help, before you came?'

'No,' she tried to twist away from him so she could think better, 'Tim only asked that someone should come and visit him. But I don't really mind!'

Damon Voulgaris ignored this. 'See what I mean, little fool! Your precious sister-in-law——'

'I'm sure she had nothing to do with it,' Tara faltered, almost tearfully. 'And will you kindly stop calling me a little fool!'

He ignored this, too. 'Veronica probably had nothing to do with getting you here, but she is obviously quite willing to accept you as an unpaid servant. I spoke with the girls in the kitchen, Tara, so it's no use denying it. Isn't she staying in bed until lunch time each day, putting up her elegant feet for the rest of the afternoon, while you fetch and carry?'

'Please!' Tara stared at him desperately, knowing she had to stop him. 'You've got it all wrong!' Trying to forget Veronica's constant stream of orders, her occasional sly digs, Tara sought to excuse her. 'She's tired, that's all, and I've only been here three days. I don't want to be disloyal to Tim, but perhaps it would be better if he let the boatyard go and concentrated on the taverna instead.'

His mouth tight, Damon looked back at her. 'You should know the truth, Tara. It is the boatyard, not the taverna, that is keeping them, which will save them. The taverna hasn't made a profit for years, but if Veronica would co-operate, it would tide them over until the boatyard really got on its feet.'

Damon appeared to know a great deal. Bemused, Tara wondered if what he told her could be true, and if it was why hadn't either Tim or Veronica explained. It would surely have been easy enough. 'Tim didn't say anything,' she admitted weakly. 'It's possibly because we haven't seen each other for years and are more like strangers. I'm sure he'll get around to telling me everything eventually.'

'I wouldn't bank on it,' Damon rejoined sarcastically. 'Married men don't usually go in for telling their young sisters everything. But I'm warning you, Tara, if he continues loading his work on to you, I will make things so uncomfortable for him he will be forced to leave the island.'

One shock was following another too rapidly. She shook. 'You wouldn't!'

'I would.'

Aghast, she stared at him blindly, seeing his dark brows drawn together, his eyes glinting like steel. He wasn't the sort to make jokes, his face was stamped with such ruthless purpose that she shivered. 'Please, Damon,' she whispered, 'I don't quite understand, but I'd do anything rather than see either Tim or Veronica suffer.'

With a muttered exclamation his arms went out and he caught Tara to him. Before she could move away he was crushing her against his broad chest, just as he had done a half hour ago. 'Don't seek to tempt me with pleading, child. In the short time I've known you I've grown fond of you —in spite of our quarrels—and refuse to stand by and see you exploited.'

Feeling the roughness of his hard chest beneath her cheek, she knew again an urgent desire to cling to him. The male scent of him invaded her sensitive nostrils and her heart began beating unevenly. Yet she wouldn't be wise to take everything he uttered too seriously, to let it affect her like this. 'It's kind of you to want to help me,' she tried not to struggle for fear it incited him to deeper anger, 'but, as you yourself have just pointed out, we've only known each other a few days and I don't suppose you intend staying long ...'

As his hand lifted to caress her silky soft hair he frowned, as though she reminded him of something he would rather forget. He said slowly, 'Time can be irrelevant, but I have always had a concern for small things and those who can't always help themselves.'

Not sure that she cared for this, she stirred. Of course he might not be describing her personally. He could be speaking of his own family, his brother, whom Veronica said was staying with him, or perhaps an unfortunate friend like Greg Golden. He probably took many people under his wing.

Before she could speak, he continued, 'I'm afraid I'm going to be rather tied up for a while. Along with everything else I find I have to see someone in Athens.'

Because he sighed rather heavily, she felt depressed. 'How long will you be gone?'

'Ah,' he smiled, his arm tightening around her, 'so you do have a healthy curiosity about me. I was beginning to think my movements didn't interest you at all. I'm not sure how long I shall be away.'

'Damon!' For some reason the thought of Jonathan intruded sharply, the information he was after. Without pausing to consider a more diplomatic approach, she asked quickly, 'Do you have a visitor at your villa?'

He was curiously still, but she didn't notice. 'Yes, my half-brother.'

Oh, well, that wouldn't be Greg Golden. With relief giving strength to her voice, she exclaimed, 'Veronica said it was your stepbrother.'

He laughed so dryly, Tara flushed in horror at her own stupidity, but when she would have flinched from him his arms held her and he only spoke mildly. 'Why ask the road you know, girl? No, he is my half-brother, although few people realise I have one. My mother married again, as I told you, but her second son is a good many years younger than I am.'

Relief that Damon wasn't angry gave her the courage to voice a sudden suspicion. 'What is your brother's name?'

He paused and, as she pondered, said lightly, 'Very soon you can come to dinner and meet him, but in the little time we have left I refuse to allow you to think of other men, Tara.'

Gazing up at him, as he eased her back against the sandy bank and looked down on her, all thought of Greg Golden fled. It was as if her mind had obeyed him implicitly. As he stared at her, her heart, which was already beating too fast, accelerated nervously. 'I must go back,' she tried to edge away from him, 'Veronica will be wondering where on earth I've got to.'

'She knows very well where you are, and you can spare me an hour. We seem in more accord than usual, so don't spoil it by running away.'

'Oh, Damon ...' Her pulse fluttered, then raced as he leant nearer, his strong arms coming down on either side of her, cutting off any means of escape.

His dark eyes glittered. 'I must make sure you're going to miss me,' he drawled, as he lowered himself against her. Deaf to her half-hearted protests, the mouth which met hers was harshly insistent, punishing her for even feebly demurring by forcing her to recognise the irrefutable attraction between them. He was holding her savagely, thrusting her ruthlessly into a world entirely of the senses, careless of hurting her when her response became wholly that of a woman. There was nothing childish in the bare arms which crept around his neck, no pretence in the trembling mouth which parted naturally under the passionate pressure of his.

As she clung to him, his hands slid under the soft, clingy
top she wore and the warm, silky skin of her back flinched
before yielding to his touch. 'Don't fight me, darling,' he
whispered thickly, his hands progressing sensuously over
her, his taut muscles pressing urgently against her slender
limbs. 'You must give me something to take with me, to
keep me sane until I return.'

Still unbearably burdened by an incredible shyness,
Tara couldn't lose the feeling that she was way out of
her depth with this man who attracted her so completely.
She had only a natural instinct to guide her, no skilful
experience, no well thought out plan of action to draw
on. The latter would never have occurred to her anyway,
as she had honestly believed she would see little of Damon
Voulgaris, once they reached Polos. His presence tonight,
more than formally attentive, seemed to contradict this.
Even so she couldn't help feeling he must only be amusing
himself. If she were sensible she would be fighting him,
instead of surrendering to the inevitable flood of excitement
she knew whenever he held her.

His mouth and arms, his hard, lean body dominated, and
Tara moaned in despair as every traitorous part of her
curved closely against him. The feel of him, the male in-
sistence of him, was sweeping through her like a storm, and
his eyes held a glittery, smouldering expression which
warned her that whatever was between them was only the
beginning. The need to resist him had never been more
urgent, if she was to escape what might amount to destruct-
ion, but while her mind threw out frantic warnings, her
senses rose like a floodtide against her.

Feverishly she spoke, when he eased his hard, punishing hold fractionally. Her lips were bruised from the pressure of his, but she managed to move them. 'Please stop,
Damon. You don't know what you're doing!'

'For the first time in my life that might almost be true,'
his voice came, thickly enigmatical. 'For the first time I
seem to be reaching heights I've never before discovered.'

His mouth softened, as he crushed hers again, regardless of her whispered pleading. 'I want everything you have to give, Tara. If not now—later.'

The excitement in Tara was fiery, flooding every vein with a blazing fire, as his words deviously fanned the flames which tore through her. All her efforts to be free of him were of no avail, even her hands, which should have been assisting in pushing him away, were shamelessly entwining in his thick, dark hair. It was only the most minimal fraction of sense which gave her the strength to protest. 'You want me because you've never been denied anything.'

'If others have given, it's never been unwillingly,' his laughter was low but harshly cynical as he turned her towards the moonlight, so he could see her tense expression as his lips explored her hot face. 'You aren't going to disappoint me, are you, small one?'

Unable to reply, because suddenly a straight answer was impossible, her mouth trembled and sought his, urgent with warm desire. As he expertly parted her lips she couldn't resist the pleasure it brought, the shameless craving he aroused. Unconsciously her hands left his head to slide over the tense muscles of his back in feverish little circles. For a long time the heavy throb of the waves pounding the beach beside them seemed to beat in strange accord with their hearts.

CHAPTER SIX

Much later, as they walked back along the beach, Tara stumbled so much that Damon eventually picked her up and carried her. Carried her as though her weight was nothing and it pleased him beyond everything to have her in his arms.

'*Liebling*,' he laughed, against the warm cheek she rested confidingly against him, 'if someone were to see us they might be excused for thinking I had just recently ravaged you!'

'Oh, Damon, I'm sorry . . .'

'Be quiet, my sweet Tara. Don't try me any further tonight,' he growled. 'I don't find the role of a thwarted lover at all easy to endure. There is still within me a great desire, cruelly unsatisfied. Say much more, continue provoking me and you will find yourself once more under the cypress trees, and this time I would be deaf to your girlish pleadings!'

Near the taverna he put her gently down but paused as she would have gone straight in. 'I want you to promise me, Tara, you won't go on working as you have been doing.'

Unhappily she bent her head, wanting to keep the rather transient tranquillity which she sensed he had deliberately imposed on the passion which had threatened to overcome them, 'I'll try not to do so much,' she agreed vaguely. 'Anyway, I think it's only until Tim gets his boatyard really going.'

'Tara!' As if coming to a quick decision, Damon said curtly, 'I wasn't going to mention this, but I happen to own the boatyard, not Tim, and the work has been getting behind. I have been complaining about Tim's neglect of it, but with good cause, as it was chiefly to help him that I began this venture.'

'You—you own it!'

'Don't look so surprised, my dear.' Coolly, as he noted her indignation, he reverted to the grim, calculating man she was all too familiar with. 'Your brother hadn't enough capital, nor could he make it from the taverna or raise it elsewhere—though he tried. If the boatyard fails, which it would do very quickly should I withdraw my support, then he couldn't carry on.'

'What you're really saying,' Tara gasped, all her old resentment of Damon Voulgaris returning, 'is that, if you felt like it, you could close him down?'

Damon's mouth went grimmer still, as he read the flicker of contempt which replaced the warm glow her eyes had reflected a minute ago. 'If you're determined to be awkward, Tara, yes. That just about sums it up. The taverna hasn't been making a profit for a long time, as I've already told you. Tim would have to sell up and leave the island. So you see, Tara, when I say I won't have you wearing yourself out, you might be wise to listen to me.'

Tara's voice faltered with dismay at what she had just learnt. Bitterly she wished Tim hadn't kept it from her. That she hadn't had to learn of it in this way! 'I'll only help a little,' she said numbly.

'I'll have a word with your brother and his wife before I go.'

'That won't be necessary.'

'Allow me to be the judge of that.'

Not trying to conceal her despair, Tara gazed up at his dark face, realising they were regarding each other warily, like a pair of strangers. Gone were the warmer feelings, the friendly mockery had left his eyes completely, to be replaced by firm purpose. 'You won't do or say anything to antagonise Veronica?' Tara asked anxiously, adding with a wisdom beyond her years, 'I'm only just getting to know her and a relationship through marriage can be tricky, to begin with, anyway.'

'Veronica is much older than you, *thespinis*, and is not without fault,' he rejoined stiffly, 'but, for your sake, I promise to be tactful.'

Which was as much as she could get him to agree to.

'Go to bed,' he said quietly, as they entered the taverna. 'I'll see you again before very long.' He didn't attempt to kiss her, but there was that in his eyes which seemed to promise something and her heart was both heavy and light as she smiled at him tremulously before running upstairs.

Unfortunately the heaviness won as she sank reflectively on to the edge of her bed. Desolation flooded her until she felt she could have wept. She wasn't thinking of what Damon might be saying in the kitchen, she could only dwell on what he had told her. That it was through his charity—there couldn't be another word to describe it— that Tim and Veronica were able to live here! Though neither of them had said anything, Tara didn't for a moment believe it wasn't true. Lots of small things fell into place as she stared down unhappily at the bare boards of her room. The shabbiness of the furniture, the thread-bare linen, the shortage of even the bare necessities in the store cupboard. They did have help, but it was just for an hour or two each evening and, she suspected, poorly paid. No, there was no reason to think Damon wasn't telling the truth. The amazing thing was that she hadn't guessed sooner.

As for giving Jonathan information which might jeop-ardise Tim's position to an even greater extent, this just wasn't on any more. If Tim left the island it mustn't be through her doing. And if she betrayed facts about one of Damon Voulgaris's guests, she didn't doubt this was what would happen. She would refuse to give Jonathan so much as a hint, and she certainly wouldn't try and discover whether Greg Golden was here or not. Jonathan, at least, had a settled job and a roof—of sorts—over his head. She couldn't be a party to taking Tim's away from him.

As for herself ... Tara frowned, reluctant to ponder even briefly on her own position. It was one thing to command herself to be sensible, quite another to carry that order out. To imagine herself in love with Damon after only seven days must indeed be crazy, yet to convince herself that this was just an idle infatuation wasn't easy. He was experienced and could probably make any girl feel committed, once he had held her in his arms. She might soon get over feeling the way she did and it might do her no harm, if she kept her head. Millionaires like Damon Voulgaris must amuse themselves with every other girl they met and, to her shame, she hadn't shown herself altogether indifferent. But, so far as she was concerned, he would have no serious intentions. If she got hurt she had only herself to blame. It was no use thinking with longing of his hard arms, the strength which made her feel both safe and in danger. Damon had merely been taking what he undoubtedly felt her family owed him, and he had obviously decided one member could repay him as well as another.

Tim had left for the boatyard next morning when she ran downstairs, but to her surprise, Veronica was in the kitchen.

'Why, good morning!' She wished she had managed to conceal her astonishment when Veronica glanced at her sharply, but decided not to say anything about any interference on Damon's part, unless Veronica mentioned it herself.

Veronica did. She had something on her mind which had been festering all night. As Tara stared at her uncomfortably, Veronica poured a large cup of coffee and placed it before her with a bang.

'Oh, thank you,' Tara muttered awkwardly.

'Don't thank me!' Veronica retorted pertly, almost as if Tara had given her the opening she sought. 'Thank Damon Voulgaris and your apparent ability to get round him. He appears to believe we're ill-treating you!'

Tara felt her cheeks grow pink, which she was well aware must make her look guilty, even before she spoke. 'He didn't get it from me,' she said quickly. 'I never said a thing.'

Veronica came back with a sharp little sneer. 'Well, if that wasn't what you discussed when you were out last night, I'd like to know what you did talk about!'

Tara's eyes rested on her sister-in-law anxiously. She didn't want to be bad friends with her and could understand she felt hurt. Damon Voulgaris ought never to have come to the taverna, upsetting everyone! A horrible thought suddenly struck her. Surely he didn't own the taverna as well? Fear shook her voice so she had to take a deep breath in order to steady it. 'I'm sorry, Veronica, but you must believe it wasn't my fault. Damon caught me behind the bar and seemed to think I shouldn't be there. I gathered that he'd asked the girls a few questions when he came in here looking for you, but you can't really blame me for that. I certainly told him I didn't mind helping.'

Veronica's eyes were still full of dislike, as she stared at Tara's dewy young face. 'That's not the impression I got, and you were out for hours! Where did you go?'

'Just along the shore.'

'Damon doesn't usually take young girls wandering in the moonlight. He must have had a good reason.'

Incredulously Tara realised Veronica was jealous. She wasn't really upset that Damon had caught Tara working, she was angry because he had taken her out. But Veronica was happily married to Tim, wasn't she, so that didn't make sense. Then, recalling Veronica's unconcealed liking for flirting with the guests who were staying, she thought she might be wise not to take her obvious penchant for Damon too seriously. All the same, it might be better to humour her.

'Damon Voulgaris,' she said firmly, 'simply wanted to know how I was getting on.'

'Really!' Veronica's eyes were still suspicious.

Not so confident, Tara began improvising uncertainly. 'I think it was because he'd been kind to me on board his yacht. The walk along the beach was only so I might get some fresh air. He did say he would be asking us all to dinner.'

Instantly Veronica was mollified, at the thought of an evening spent in Damon's luxurious villa. 'I expect he'll be giving me a ring,' she smiled smugly. 'He usually does. I should warn you not to fall for him, though. I have enough to worry about without having a lovesick sister-in-law on my hands.' Taking no notice of Tara's startled expression, she added sharply, 'He prefers something a little different from your wide-eyed innocence. You should have seen the girl who came here earlier in the year, especially to be with him.'

'She stayed here?'

'Sure.' Veronica wandered over to the mirror, studying her face with appraising satisfaction. 'She stayed here, but he had her up to the villa every day. It was quite obvious she was mad about him and Tim and I were beginning to think he shared her feelings, but nothing seemed to come of it.'

'I see.'

'And you're sure of what he said about dinner?'

'He did ...'

'Oh, lovely! That will be something to look forward to.' With a noticeable improvement of temper, Veronica told Tara magnanimously that if she helped in the mornings she might have the afternoons off, but after their present guests left, there wouldn't be a lot to do, anyway.

On the second afternoon, Tara decided she would explore a little. The previous afternoon Tim had taken her to the boatyard, now she borrowed his fieldglasses and set out in the opposite direction. It would be interesting to see more of the island and, as Tim hadn't a car she could borrow as well, she would have to do it on foot. Even with a car many of the roads were little more than dirt tracks. The locals, she had discovered, usually used boats for transport as the island abounded with convenient coves, which provided safe anchorage while friends were visited.

Tara had no friends to visit. The girls who worked in the taverna lived in the village beside it and she knew no one else. But the German couples had left that morning in their small yacht and she felt she ought to make the most of her free time. Only the Frenchman remained, so there would be just one to look after until, perhaps, the occupants of another boat decided they would like to spend a few days on dry land.

So far as she knew, Damon's yacht had not arrived yet, but his villa was, according to Veronica, only a few miles away. Tara couldn't recall the distance herself, as the night Damon had driven her to the taverna it had been dark and the road had twisted. Curiosity stirred in her regarding his house and she found herself unable to resist it. While she didn't intend going too near, she knew a suddenly urgent desire to see what it looked like. Not ready to admit it was really a glimpse of the man who owned it she was after, she assured herself she was only showing a healthy interest in the island.

Having jokingly confided in Veronica as to what she intended doing, she had been surprised when Veronica had given her brief instructions. 'Take care Damon doesn't catch you, though,' Veronica had warned. 'He can be very touchy regarding his privacy.'

'Damon's in Athens.'

'Ah, yes, of course.'

Veronica had been quite friendly these past two days, yet Tara was aware there was still some tension. It wouldn't do to upset her again.

Damon's villa was nearer than Tara had expected, but it could have been because of the different track which Veronica advised her to take. It wound up through orange and lemon groves, high above the sea. Around a clump of the familiar cypress Tara came on the house quite suddenly and was startled to find herself so near. The way she had come must almost have halved the distance.

Below her the villa lay in resplendent whiteness, looking comfortably large without being ostentatious. The grounds, she guessed, were extensive. She didn't need Tim's fieldglasses to see this. From her elevated position Tara could see, without the glasses, very clearly. The gardens seemed formally laid out with green lawns and lots of white paving, the later being decorated with numerous small statuettes, in stone and blue and white marble. There were columns and pillars. These appeared to be in marble, too, although from this distance it was difficult to tell as they were covered with green climbing plants which, in turn, were smothered in a profusion of brilliantly coloured flowers. Further on, away from the house, she detected a huge swimming pool, gleaming, with a betraying splash of blue against the green and white of its surroundings.

The whole place looked deserted, which wasn't surprising as Damon was away. Idly, before leaving, and not really sure why she did so, Tara lifted Tim's fieldglasses indifferently. It seemed silly, having brought them, not to have a closer look around. Startled, she saw, when she lifted them to her eyes, that the pool area was not deserted, as she had first thought. Tucked away in one corner of it two figures lay on flat mattresses beside the still water. One was a girl; the other, Tara could have sworn, was Damon Voulgaris!

Feeling cold to the very tips of her trembling fingers, Tara continued staring, completely unaware for a moment of what she was doing. There was no reason why Damon should not be down there. She had thought he was in Athens, but where he was or what he was doing had really nothing to do with her. It was she who was in the wrong, sitting up here watching him. Yet Tara couldn't have moved if someone had offered her a million pounds. Even her limbs felt frozen.

There was worse to come. The scene changed, to convince Tara there was rarely any comfort to be derived from not minding one's own business. The girl moved nearer to Damon, leaning over him as he lay, clad only in swimming trunks, beside her. As the girl bent to kiss him, Tara saw Damon's arms come out and take hold of the slim figure so near his.

Shock kept the fieldglasses almost glued to Tara's tear-filled eyes, though she immediately jerked them away from the embracing couple. As she did so, she caught a glimpse of another man leaving the house, carrying a tray of drinks. He was of medium height and slender, with a shock of golden hair. It was none other, Tara knew she wasn't mistaken, but Greg Golden!

Retracing her footsteps, Tara walked a full mile before she allowed herself to rest. It seemed suddenly imperative that she put some distance between herself and the villa. She wasn't sure what she felt like, she only knew she never wanted to feel like this again. Her heart was pounding, she felt sick and had only a hysterical desire to cry. Damon was here. He wasn't in Athens. He was there, in his own garden, making love to a woman who Tara judged was both glamorous and beautiful, kissing her, as he had kissed Tara only a few nights ago on the beach. That Greg Golden was there, too, didn't hold Tara's interest for more than a passing second.

At last she forced herself to continue back to the taverna. Tim was still at the boatyard, but Veronica was in the sitting room.

'Oh, hello,' she glanced over the top of the book she was reading indifferently. 'Did you find the villa, then?'

'Yes.' Tara was conscious her voice might sound flat. Strange and flat, because that was the way she felt and she hadn't the strength left to disguise it. There was also self-loathing within her and anger, but the latter hadn't yet had time to gain full momentum. No one could be blamed that she had allowed herself to fall in love with a man who

had only been amusing himself at her expense. She ought
to have heeded Veronica's hints and her own intuition
that Damon Voulgaris might make careless love to every
other woman he met, without a thought for anything but
his own pleasure.

'See anyone?'

Scarcely aware of anything but her own searing pain,
Tara answered absently, 'Greg Golden—I think.'

'The singer?' The lowering of heavy eyelids hid Veronica's sudden interest.

'Yes.'

Afterwards, Tara was to remember how she had been
too absorbed with her own unhappiness to notice that
Veronica hadn't asked another question.

'Tim has promised to take us sailing this evening,'
Veronica changed the subject abruptly. 'I hope he doesn't
change his mind.'

It was on the next afternoon, just as Tara returned from
a dejected walk along the beach, that Veronica announced
they were invited to Damon's villa that evening for dinner.

'Oh, no!' Tim, who was burrowing in a kitchen drawer
for some tool he had lost, threw back his head in exaspera-
tion. 'Damn it all, Veronica, I can't spare the time! I've
two orders which must be finished. I'd planned to work
late.'

'I'm not keen to go either,' Tara tried to hide her revulsion. 'Couldn't we refuse?'

Tim sighed, with a quick glance at his wife's cold face.
'I wish we could, infant, but, apart from Veronica here
having a liking for dining in style, I'm just not in the
position to offend—Mr Voulgaris!'

Tara didn't ask why, having no desire to embarrass
him. She already knew much and had guessed the rest
and had no intention of adding to Tim's humiliation. 'Why
don't you and Veronica go? I'll stay here and keep an eye
on things.'

'Oh no, you don't!' Veronica turned on her so sharply

Tara was astonished. 'Damon said all of us and all of us it's going to be—much as I wouldn't mind leaving you both behind.'

In the end they did go, every one of them. The Frenchman, greatly amused, begged to be allowed to make his own dinner, so Tara's last excuse was taken from her. After going to such lengths to see Damon's villa the previous day, she dared not call too much attention to herself by continuing to refuse. She would have hated Veronica to discover the misery which threatened to swamp her entirely. It was probably time she grew up a little and learnt not to take what Damon had probably only intended as a little light flirtation so seriously.

After dressing carefully in a long, silk dress, she applied extra make-up, taking particular care with her lipstick and mascara. Her smooth, flawless skin didn't really need it, but she was determined that Damon shouldn't guess the weight of unhappiness which made her cheeks far too pale. Her hair she brushed rather carelessly over her shoulders, glad that it was fluffy enough to look nice whichever way she wore it. She didn't feel up to arranging it, tonight, in one of the more modern styles her age group had been favouring lately. When Veronica called all she had left to do was slip her feet into a pair of strapped sandals and she was ready.

Damon had sent a car for them and they reached his villa at the arranged hour. That he hadn't bothered to get in touch with her himself, as he had promised, seemed to Tara a clear indication that he had transferred his interest elsewhere. She supposed she should be feeling grateful, rather than ashamed, that she had received due warning of this by seeing him embracing another girl in his garden. Otherwise she might have made a terrible fool of herself by allowing him to see how much she cared.

He came to meet them himself, and, for all she hung back, Tara was eventually forced to speak. 'Good evening,' she managed, with a vague smile, her eyes reaching no higher than his deeply cleft chin.

'It's good to see you again, Tara.' His voice, warmly friendly, brought her gaze quickly to meet his and her smile wobbled dangerously before something unreadable but slightly dangerous in his eyes. For a moment she had the odd impression that he would like to have whisked her over the courtyard, away from the others, but as if remembering where he was, he turned reluctantly from her and began talking to Tim.

Veronica, as they went in, shot her an acid glance which clearly blamed Tara for the way in which Damon, after a briefly polite greeting, had ignored her. Again Tara suspected, with some bewilderment, that though married to Tim, Veronica was definitely attracted to Damon Voulgaris and would resent anyone who appeared to steal even a little of his attention while she was around. What, Tara wondered despairingly, was Veronica going to think if this other girl was here tonight?

Damon's house was as attractive inside as Tara had thought it would be, but she was surprised to find it was far from luxuriously furnished. Only the thick rugs on the floor and deep seats around the fire gave a hint of the comfort which might be found here when winter storms hit the island. On the whole, the rooms were bare, the heavy furnishings practical rather than decorative, although there was no doubting the quality of them.

The lounge he led them to was of medium size. Two people were seated there. One, whom Tara immediately recognised from TV and numerous cuttings Jonathan had shown her, rose to his feet as they came in. It was Greg Golden, and she had some difficulty in hiding her surprise when Damon introduced him as Greg Davidson. But it was nothing to her astonishment when he went on to say that Greg was his half-brother.

'You were asking about him, Tara,' he said coolly.

'Now you can have the doubtful pleasure of meeting him.'

Tara had never met a star before. At least, Damon hadn't introduced him as a star, but she couldn't be mistaken. After a few more moments she realised he wasn't going to mention it; he must intend hiding Greg's real identity. Well, if this was the way he wanted it, she certainly wasn't going to say anything. Having learnt how he practically owned Tim's business, she wouldn't dare. If Damon really was Greg's half-brother then naturally he would be protecting him from all the newshounds who were trying desperately to discover the whereabouts of the famous Greg Golden.

Greg shook hands with them all, then introduced his fiancée. Tara had been conscious of a tall, blonde girl, whose hair colouring almost matched Greg's, standing near the terrace windows at the end of the room with a look of complete boredom on her rather hard but good-looking face. Smiling charmingly, Greg drew her nearer. 'I'd like you to meet my fiancée, Angela Felton.'

On the way to dinner, Tara was still feeling vaguely surprised that her suspicions had been confirmed beyond doubt. This was Lord Felton's daughter, and while Tara couldn't be sure she was the 'right little bitch' Jonathan had called her, she certainly didn't seem as pleasant as her fiancé. One thing Tara was sure about was that she was the girl who had been in Damon's arms the previous afternoon. Knowing this she felt a return of the same sickness of heart which had attacked her then. She watched dully as Miss Felton slipped her arm through Damon's, rather than that of her fiancé, and smiled up at him with a blatant adoration which, Tara heard, brought from Veronica a small, hissing breath.

As they left the lounge Tara found herself wishing bleakly that she had never come. What with one thing and another, she seemed to have wasted her time coming to Polos at all. She had seen little of Tim since she had arrived, and achieved anything but a satisfactory relationship with Veronica and, to top everything, she had fallen in love with a man who had only been playing with her. In other words, she'd managed to make a complete fool of herself, all in the space of barely two weeks!

On entering the dining room she was so busy moodily contemplating her own folly that she failed to see Damon detach himself firmly from Angela Felton and make his way to her side. She actually blinked when he spoke to her.

'Will you sit by me?' he asked softly. 'I would like you beside me.'

'If you like.' She looked at him anxiously, suddenly very shy, wanting desperately to believe he had only been amusing himself with Angela Felton. While it was perhaps not very charitable to wish this on the other girl, she fancied Miss Felton was more than able to look after herself. Besides, if this girl was Greg's fiancée, there surely was no chance of Damon having serious thoughts about her. It hurt that he had succumbed to the popular habit of making love whenever the opportunity presented itself, but she had never imagined Damon to be any saint. Casting caution to the wind, she let the warmth in his voice seduce her a little, and as she met his eyes her own glowed.

Damon, as though making up for any pain he might have caused her, was very attentive. Yet, under the glittering dislike of two pairs of eyes—Angela's and Veronica's—Tara didn't feel altogether comfortable, especially when, as the meal got under way and the wine flowed, Veronica wasn't over-careful about hiding her jealousy. When, under cover of a particularly loud piece of conversation, Damon bent near and whispered, 'Miss me?' she saw Veronica's eyes narrow with sudden rage, as his lips almost touched her ear.

Torn between the choice of snapping or smiling at

him, she was giving away shamelessly to the latter when
Veronica's sharp voice shattered the feeling of warmth
between them.

She was addressing Greg. 'I was interested when Tara
told me yesterday that you're really Greg Golden. She
saw you when she was up here yesterday afternoon, but
even if she hadn't been spying on you, I should have
guessed. Or would I?' her laughter was high. 'No, maybe
not. You've never been here before and we're so out of
touch on Polos. Without Tara's help I might never have
recognised you, especially as Damon never said . . .'

There was a moment's dreadful silence in which even
Veronica must have felt the atmosphere. She went pale
but looked in no way repentant.

Before Tim could tell her to shut up, as he had appeared
too startled to do at once, Veronica rushed on, as
though she couldn't stop. 'You didn't know Tara is a
journalist, did you, Damon?'

'My God!' He was on his feet, his face marble-cold as
he stared down on a speechless Tara. 'No, I did not!'

Veronica wasn't finished yet. 'Apparently all England
is agog about Greg Golden's disappearance, Damon. Jonathan, Tim's brother, is a journalist, too. He's rung three
times, asking for Tara, to see if she had any news for
him.'

Tim exploded helplessly, 'Veronica, you never said!'

'If I'd told you,' she retorted defiantly, 'you'd only have
blown your top, or felt responsible.'

Shooting a quick, puzzled glance at his sister's white
face, Tim shook his head. 'But why say anything now?'

'Because . . .' Suddenly Veronica's nerve crumpled and
she too jumped to her feet. 'I don't know why I said anything!' she almost shrieked. 'Perhaps,' she paused, and
Tara, though shocked and bewildered, could see her groping wildly for an excuse, 'I think my conscience got the
better of me, or fright! Jonathan talked of having a horde
of reporters here, once he knew for sure, and after all

Damon has done for us, I just couldn't stand by and let this happen. Anyway,' she added sullenly, 'if Damon had discovered and known we hadn't—we hadn't told him, he might have thrown us off the island, and you wouldn't have liked that, would you?'

Damon still hadn't said anything, other than his first bitter exclamation, and Tara couldn't seem to find the courage to even glance at him.

Into the short, taut silence, Angela emitted a small, hysterical scream. 'Greg came all this way to escape publicity and you went to so much trouble to help him, Damon. He—all three of us, need this breathing space to sort ourselves out, you know this as well as anybody! You can't just stand by and let a little chit of a journalist ruin everything!'

Tim interrupted staunchly, apparently not quite so willing to condemn his sister as the others, 'But you aren't a journalist, are you, Tara?'

'Are you?' Quickly in control of himself again, Damon dropped down beside her, his voice quite gentle, as if, like Tim, he was reluctant to believe the worst.

'No, well ...' Suddenly despondent, Tara remembered the local paper, the work she had done on it, about which she had so foolishly confided in Veronica. There had never seemed an opportunity to tell Tim. 'Yes, but ...' she stammered, searching desperately for the right words to explain.

No match for a man like Damon Voulgaris, once he got started, she was aghast to hear his voice turn to steel again, his mistaken tenderness forgotten. Obviously regretted, too, she could see. 'Did you arrange anything with your brother in England, Tara?'

'I—I'm not sure. Yes, I suppose so,' she confessed, having to grip the edge of her chair tightly in order to control the fright which was shaking her. 'In a way,' she whispered, closing her eyes helplessly against his harsh stare.

He rose, as she sat endeavouring to make her numbed brain work, to try and tell them how this was all too ridiculous, but nothing would come.

She heard Damon saying, 'I think, Tim, if you take your wife home and leave Tara to me, I might be able to work something out.'

Tim declined fiercely, 'She's my sister, Damon, and I'm not sure yet that she's done anything wrong. I just can't abandon her.'

Suddenly Greg exclaimed, 'Whatever happens, Damon, the press mustn't know I'm here. Supposing we have to throttle the little ...'

'Be quiet!' Damon thundered, furiously. 'All of you!' He turned to Tim curtly, like a man driven almost beyond endurance. 'Listen, Curtis, I promise no harm will come to your sister, but I must have time to decide what to do. I want to talk to her and I don't think it will help if you stay around.'

'Tara——' Tim began, clearly not knowing what to do for the best.

Tara found her voice with difficulty, as he stared at her anxiously. 'I think Mr Voulgaris is right, Tim.' She sought harder to reassure him when he frowned. 'I'm quite willing to talk because I don't think I have much to hide, but it would be better if you went back to the taverna.'

Damon waved away the servants who were bringing in the next course. 'I don't think any of us has any appetite left,' he glanced grimly around the table as the servants went out again. 'The next time you come, Tim, I hope it will be in happier circumstances.'

Five minutes later Tim and Veronica had gone and Tara found herself in a small room, at the end of a passage with Damon Voulgaris. Greg had appeared to collapse in a fit of dramatic depression—Tara could find no other way to describe it. Already sick at heart, she had felt much worse on hearing him groan and implore Damon loudly to 'save him'. She couldn't remember ever seeing a man act like that before, but then she supposed that was what Greg was—an actor. Angela Felton had startled Tara, too, the way she had stared, almost contemptuously, as her fiancé had thrown himself wildly into the nearest chair. He had chosen, she noticed, a very comfortable one.

Though completely numb from Veronica's unexpected vindictiveness, Tara felt astonished at both of them. Greg Golden's nerves were shot to pieces, and Angela's attitude couldn't be much help. For all her hurt, Tara felt she could sympathise with Damon if this was what he had to contend with. As he closed the door of the room, however, her pity changed to nervousness again. From the look on his face all he wanted was revenge!

Coming nearer, he stood watching her coldly, until apprehension drove her to speak. In the brief moments of retrospect which were all the short journey from the lounge had allowed, she couldn't think she had committed any great crime, but it wasn't encouraging that Damon's expression said exactly the opposite. He didn't seem to resemble, even remotely, the man who had only a few days ago held her in his arms and made passionate love to her.

'Damon,' hastily she moistened dry lips and took a deep breath, 'Damon,' she tried again, 'if only you'd listen, I can explain.'

CHAPTER SEVEN

'EXPLAIN? Really?' Damon drawled sarcastically, as his eyes took in the demure neckline, the simple hair-style, the hurt lurking at the back of the bewildered eyes of the girl before him, and his own only grew harder. 'You really strung me along, didn't you, Tara? All nervous young uncertainty, a little temper, a few tears, then so softly yielding. I almost fell for it, like a fool! Your brother Jonathan knew exactly what he was doing when he sent you. Not only did you almost get what you were after, you succeeded in arousing my interest, too.'

'Please, Damon!'

'You wouldn't have had to beg, you know, if you'd played your cards right.'

Feeling none of this could actually be happening, Tara raised a defensive hand, as if unconsciously warding something off. 'You don't understand!' she whispered, wondering, as she felt his eyes already condemning her, how she was going to make him.

Anger flared in him and she could feel it as he put a hand to her hair, as though he would like to tear it from her scalp and enjoy hearing her moan with pain. His voice, when he spoke, told of control barely held and it frightened her nearly as much as his hands.

'Don't worry, Tara, I'm going to give you every chance of explaining, because it's important I should know everything that's going on. Important for the woman it's just possible I might love, as much as anything else.'

Despair whipped through Tara, then. So it had been no idle embrace she had witnessed in the garden from the top of the hill. Naturally he was being cautious about it, but it was quite clear whom he meant. Her eyes blazing

114

from an inexplicable sense of loss, she said tersely, 'I think you must all be going crazy! I have nothing to hide. I haven't done anything wrong.'

'You're a journalist.'

Almost wryly she shook her head. 'I worked on a local paper, part-time.'

'But with ambitions?'

'I did my best, but that's not the same thing.'

The twist to Damon's lips was a sneer, not a grin. Harshly his hands came down on her shoulders. 'Yet you felt confident enough to undertake this assignment for your brother in England!'

Quickly, because of the flames running through her from his fingers, Tara wrenched away, but the eyes she lifted to his were eloquent of a sudden need to convince him of her innocence. 'You must listen! I'd scarcely heard of Greg Golden before I came here. I certainly knew nothing of his fiancée. Apart from—from what ...'

'Yes?' he prompted curtly, as she floundered.

'Just what Jonathan told me,' she hedged weakly, frightened of stirring Damon's wrath to an even greater extent by repeating Jonathan's comments about Angela Felton. 'He didn't say much. He doesn't even know she's on Polos.'

'How did he know Greg was here?' asked Damon sharply.

'He didn't. He was only guessing.'

'Guessing?'

'Well, he had a—a tip-off, he said.'

'Ah, yes!' Damon jeered softly. 'Those small hints which are the veritable bread of life for our friends in the press.'

'Do you have to be so horrible?' Tara flared, trying hard not to remember how he had looked the last time she had seen him, how gentle that forceful mouth had been against her own. Now he was so grimly forbidding, she realised she could expect little mercy from it. 'Anyway,' she shuddered, 'people like Greg must be well used to publicity. You couldn't deny they often encourage it, and though, in this instance, the press may be more than normally curious, once they know where he is they would very likely leave him alone.'

'The press rarely leave anyone alone if they think there's a story to tell which might interest the public.'

Tara sighed, torn between indignant anger and a kind of desperate need to get through to him. 'I've been trying to explain, Damon, I wasn't going to have anything to do with it.'

'Yet you sneaked up here yesterday, trying to find out as much as you could.' Disbelief hardened his face, made his eyes glitter scornfully on her nervous shrinking. 'It's a pity you didn't try making a friend of your sister-in-law before you began your campaign.'

'I never—I'm sure I never did anything to offend Veronica. I don't know why she said what she did!'

'That's more than even I'm willing to swallow,' Voulgaris exclaimed tightly. 'You come to the hill behind the house, very probably with a pair of borrowed binoculars.' As Tara flushed scarlet, his eyes narrowed derisively and he went on, 'You return to the taverna and tell her you have seen Greg Golden, while your brother in England rings continually for news. Don't you believe this would be enough to scare her half to death, seeing how I own the boatyard, the taverna and damn well almost everything else they possess! I think I can understand Veronica's hysteria, if you can't.'

As he paused impatiently, Tara said quickly, 'This was why I changed my mind, when I learnt how you practically own them. I realised they could be in a worse position than Jonathan, if I did anything to displease you, but I never dreamt Veronica suspected. She must have jumped to a lot of conclusions, but that still doesn't explain why she had to come out with them tonight.'

Damon's glance was so cold on her white face, Tara knew she was trying to impress him in vain. 'What else did you see from the top of the hill?' he enquired suavely.

'How did you know where I was?' Desperately she played for time.

'I can guess.'

'I saw Greg—nothing much else,' she managed, as he was obviously not going to be denied an answer.

'What else?' He was dangerously insistent.

'If you must know,' she clenched her hands tight so he shouldn't guess the pain, 'I saw you with your half-brother's fiancée.'

'So,' he jeered softly, 'you didn't like what you saw?'

Trying to deceive him was like battering one's head against a stone wall. 'I think you're despicable!' she cried, heedlessly. 'You make love to me and say you have to be away on business, but instead you go straight to another woman's arms. A woman who belongs to some-one else.'

His face went black as he stepped nearer, catching Tara ruthlessly to him again, his hands crushing the soft skin of her upper arms. 'Don't you know, Tara, how I enjoy making love to any number of women? Worthless ones, like yourself, I find particularly amusing! You come here under the guise of an innocent young girl, while actually working for a newspaper—one, if I'm not mistaken, re-nowned for its racy scandal. There are others, like Angela, who while betrothed to another man seek the excitement of forbidden arms. Maybe they are just as despicable as you, my dear, but at least women like Angela are usually willing to pay for their sins by going the whole way. They don't pretend to be naïve little virgins! But whisper one detri-mental word to Greg about his fiancée, Tara, and who can say where his shattered nerves might drive him.'

This, on top of everything else Damon had said, had Tara's legs trembling. Instantly her own troubles seemed less beside the size of another's. 'Nerves?' she whispered blankly.

'His doctor has warned him what might happen if he doesn't give himself a break.'

The way Damon had slaughtered her paled a little. 'Is this why he doesn't want anyone to know where he is?'

'Partly.' Damon was coldly cautious.

Tara turned her eyes from him, suddenly shivering. 'I think I understand. It must be difficult for all of you. I'll go, Damon.'

'You'll—what?'

'I said, I'll go now. You have my word I'll not say anything and—and you can't want to prolong this conversation.'

'Your word!' he ejaculated cynically, ignoring the latter half of her sentence. 'That's the last thing I would take. You're not going anywhere, my dear. You're staying right here! You've been having fun at my expense,' he paused, his eyes going deliberately over her, resting pointedly on her mouth, 'now it's my turn. Besides, no matter what I was prepared to accept, Greg's state of mind couldn't stand the thought of you being on the loose, free to betray his whereabouts. He has to have time to sort his life out in peace and he knows I'm going to see he gets it.'

Tara's huge green eyes widened with shock. 'How do you mean, I've been having fun at your expense?' she stammered bitterly. 'I don't recall having had much pleasure from this trip at all. I wish I'd never come here!'

'You enjoyed yourself well enough, making me believe you were beginning to care for me,' he rejoined harshly, 'but that was only to get information, wasn't it? Each time you surrendered your enticing little body it was solely with this in view. Now you don't appreciate a little turning of the tables.'

Her face a haunted white, she stared up at him, feeling his incensed breath scorching her cheeks. He was furious because he thought he had just been a means to an end. Well, perhaps it was better this way. Better than that he should suspect she had fallen in love with him! Closing

her eyes briefly against the glare in his, she protested
sullenly, 'You can't keep me here!'

'Can't I?'

'No.' Trying to speak calmly, she pointed out, 'Anyone
could have told the newspapers where Greg was. The
servants, people on the island, tourists. You haven't tried
to hide him, so why get in a state about me?'

'There has been no need to hide him,' Damon retorted,
curtly, 'as no one would have betrayed him. The servants
and islanders are completely loyal, as well as knowing
when they're well off, and your brother is wholly reliant
on me. Should Tim talk to a newspaper man, what would
there be in it for him?'

'I see,' she said bitterly, seeing all too clearly.

'You do?' he smiled with mock gratification. 'I'm so
glad!' One of his hands left her arm to push her chin up,
so as to make sure she understood. 'You'll stay here for a
few days, until Greg feels like facing the world again.'

'I can't . . .'

'If you insist on refusing I will close the boatyard,
everything Tim has. Come on, Tara, the only choice I'm
really allowing you is that of giving in gracefully.'

'You can't be serious?' she cried, the tremor in her
voice belying her bravado.

'You'll even sleep with me,' he promised steadily, 'so I
can watch every move you make.'

'You're detestable!' she choked, before his tigerish grin,
suspecting he was just taunting her but unable to prevent
herself rising to the bait. 'That's the last thing I would
do!'

He smiled again, a smile of sheer mockery, ignoring her
shocked protests. 'I'm sure, like many members of your
profession, you've been in many tight corners before and
managed to survive.' He turned, keeping hold of her still.
'I will take you to your room. This is something I'm beginning to excel at, is it not? Only this time we are not on
the yacht and things are rather different. This time I

will not be spoiling you, but neither will I spare you. For the duration of your stay here, I will treat you as I feel inclined.'

As he led her upstairs Tara felt too bemused to make any further objection. If she did she had no doubt he would easily resort to brute force, but apart from this, she wouldn't allow herself to take his harsh threats too seriously. She wasn't sure about his intention of keeping her prisoner, but sleeping together was something else again. He might perhaps put her next door to him, which would be bad enough, but he wouldn't flout convention so blatantly as to have her in the same room as himself! Once on her own, if she stayed calm, she might soon find some means of escape. Doors could be locked, but there were always windows.

They met no one as they traversed long corridors from the top of wide stairs. The house seemed silent and deserted. Tara shivered. But it wasn't until he thrust her into a room containing twin beds that she began to know a deepening of the fear she had tried to push to the back of her mind.

'You can't mean it!' she breathed, trying to strengthen her voice as he stood watching her contemplatively, but without emotion as she stared, aghast, at the beds. 'If I'm to stay here,' she added distractedly, when he made no reply, 'I demand privacy.'

'You demand!' He caught at her silk-clad shoulder, his lean fingers pressing the bone painfully. 'You must be out of your head, girl. Those who have no respect for the privacy of others should know better than to expect it for themselves.'

'What about your precious Angela?' she countered wildly. 'What if I were to tell your brother you not only had his fiancée in your arms, you were kissing her as well. Don't you think, all things considered, you'd be wiser to let me go?'

'So you saw that, too, did you?' No hint of remorse.

'And was this to be relayed to Jonathan, along with everything else?'

Tara had a sudden feeling she wasn't helping her own cause, but she refused to speak.

'Was it?' he demanded savagely.

Still she stared at him irresolutely, not saying anything, keeping her mouth tight shut for fear she was tempted to say too much and only made things worse.

Hurtfully his hands slid down her bare arms then returned to her shoulders, which were braced in dazed defiance. His eyes were hard and implacable. 'Like all your sort you've plenty of courage until caught in a trap of your own making. Even now you're trying to bolster your deceitful, cowardly little heart by telling yourself hopefully that Damon Voulgaris never means the half of what he says. Well, let me tell you, Miss Curtis, I've suffered a lot at the hands of your profession. You've torn me to pieces more times than I deserved. Greg aside, it's going to feel good to extract some revenge. It will do you good, too, to be on the receiving end for a change.'

'A man's position in life sometimes has to be paid for,' she gasped angrily, as the feeling from his hands disturbed her thought pattern so much she was scarcely aware of what she was saying.

'That's something I soon learnt to accept,' he replied indifferently. 'And I haven't made a lot of money without learning how to be entirely ruthless, when the occasion warrants it. Certainly a lot of my softer emotions died in the struggle to the top—and don't think you're going to be able to revive them. Before I'm through with you, you may never want to see another newspaper again.'

His hands fell from her shoulders as she started apprehensively. 'Make yourself at home,' his level gaze held hers relentlessly, 'I'll be back in a few minutes with some food as you had no dinner. I shouldn't like the pangs of hunger to triumph over the other kinds of feelings I intend arousing in you.'

He locked the door as he went out but, true to his word, he returned very quickly with a tray. Tara hadn't moved from where he had left her standing, her limbs, as well as her mind, seeming frozen with despair. Arrogantly he said, 'If this is not all eaten up by the time I come to bed, then I'll personally sit over you until it is.'

As he left the key turned again in the lock. Tara thought she had never heard a more ominous sound. As she stared at the tightly closed door she realised blankly that Damon was cutting off every means of escape. He just wasn't taking any chances! She had thought it crazy, that ever since she'd met Damon Voulgaris her one instinctive wish had been to avoid him, but in this her intuition had been proved right, as hadn't she finished up in a terrible situation? How could Jonathan have put her at risk like this? He must have known the kind of man she'd have to deal with. It was a bitter pill to swallow that, like a blind fool, she had sailed blithely on, trusting everyone, never for a moment seriously thinking there could be any terrible repercussions. Never had she given a thought to any actual danger.

Now the fate of some journalists who travelled the world came to haunt her. There were those who were shot, blown up, captured, all in pursuit of the stories which a news-hungry public demanded. It came back to her, one particularly narrow escape Jonathan had had when covering a very tricky assignment in Africa. Quite by accident they had heard of it and, when her mother had worried, Tara had wondered indignantly why Jonathan couldn't be content with what he could pick up locally.

Her father had pointed out, 'People would soon tire of Mrs Bloggs' adventures at the kitchen sink, Tara. And remember, very few reporters are ever killed.'

True, Tara supposed despondently, her glance going dismally over the beautifully arranged tray which Damon had placed on a low table, but it was no consolation to recall this in her present position. Damon believed she had deliberately tricked him, had encouraged his love-making with this end in view. It must rankle that a man in his position had apparently been taken in by a girl like herself, and she shuddered to think what sort of revenge he was devising. There was undoubtedly a desire to protect his half-brother. This she could understand as hadn't she two brothers herself, but most of all, she was unhappily convinced, his present actions stemmed as much from a determination to avenge himself on a girl who'd had the nerve to try and make a fool of him.

Tara's breath caught in her throat as she considered this, as she sat down by the small table and stared at her tray. Surely Damon didn't really believe she had been able to pretend the way she'd felt in his arms? His mouth on hers, warm and demanding, had aroused such feeling within her, an excitement she had never known before. She could still feel the shiver of peculiar heat over her skin, like the pricking of a thousand needles where his mouth touched. When he had first kissed her she had been frightened of such feelings, but on the beach that other night, the fright had changed to something else. It had still lingered, but his tenderness had aroused other, stronger emotions, emotions she hadn't wanted to fight. With a trembling reluctance she admitted that had Damon really tried he might easily have swept aside the basic principles which her parents had so conscientiously tried to instil into her.

Desperately, in order to prevent herself thinking of this any longer, she switched her thoughts to Veronica. What on earth, she wondered painfully, had made Veronica say what she had? Somehow she didn't think it had been premeditated. Veronica had been frightened afterwards, she had still looked nervous when Tim had taken her away. There had even been the impression that she regretted her outburst even more when, because of the information she'd revealed, Damon had insisted Tara stayed here.

Tara, already very aware that her sister-in-law was a

woman swayed often by less than sensible impulses, had been sure this wasn't the outcome Veronica had expected and she would have given anything to have taken back what she had said. But of course, it had been too late and already Tara was discovering that the spoken word could be just as lethal as the written one, given the right circumstances.

Finishing the meal she hadn't really tasted, which only fear had impelled her to eat, she took a closer look at her surroundings, something she had been too tense to do before. There was every comfort here. Modern beds stood side by side, joined by a twin headboard with fitted reading lights, a supply of new books. These were on one of the polished shelves along with a carafe of crystal clear water and two glasses. The rugs on the tiled floor were deep and behind the solid furniture the walls were rough white plaster, the whole giving an impression of cosy intimacy Tara would have rather done without.

Yet she didn't get the feeling of the room being used regularly, not by Damon at any rate. His large frame would fit more easily into a bed of larger dimensions than the two which were here. Nor did she really believe, deep down, that he would carry out his threat of sleeping here tonight. That would just have been said to frighten and punish her. She didn't doubt he would keep her locked in, but to sleep beside her would be as damaging to his reputation as hers.

Noticing another door at the side of the room, she leaped quickly to her feet, but it only led to a bathroom. An extremely comprehensive bathroom; she found a shower and a beautiful sunken bath, together with a supply of thick, fleecy towels and every luxurious appointment she could think of, but there was no door to the corridor outside, no route through which she might have escaped and fled back to the taverna.

Returning to the bedroom, Tara sat down again, not sure

what to do. She felt frightened, alone, on the verge of bewildered hysteria. She was weary yet she couldn't get into bed as, she kept telling herself, she had no intention of staying. Surely, when she didn't go back to the taverna, Tim would come looking for her? He would know what to do. He would never leave her at the mercy of a man like Damon Voulgaris; he wouldn't be frightened of confronting him if he really had to.

So busy was she fighting tears, Tara didn't see the door thrust ajar until Damon strode through it, carrying an armful of clothes.

'I've borrowed these from Angela. They'll at least see you through one night.'

When he swung round after dropping them carelessly on one of the beds, she was standing looking at him, her face pale.

'I've told you I can't stay here!'

Over his shoulder as he went out again, he said coldly, 'I'll give you five minutes exactly to get into bed. Then I'll be back.'

Shuddering, as tears of helplessness fell, Tara wondered what she did now. She didn't seem to have much option. Vowing vengeance, as she sobbed, she groped blindly at the clothes he had brought. The scrap of silk, she saw, was a nightdress, the matching robe scarcely thicker but possessing a wide sash, which she supposed was something to be thankful for. There was also a silk shirt and a pair of shorts. These she flung on to the nearest chair as she flew with the rest of the things to the bathroom. She had suddenly little doubt that if she didn't obey Damon to the letter he would put her to bed himself.

The nightdress, when she put it on, made her blush, but the anger she felt helped dry her tears. It helped get her thinking again, too, and it quickly occurred to her how a chair could often be wedged successfully against a door.

No sooner had she thought of it than the deed was done

and it was with a pounding but slightly happier heart
that she lay in bed, listening to Damon knocking in vain
to get in.

'Tara!' his voice came curtly through the panels, 'I
don't wish to break anything, so will you please come and
remove whatever it is you've used and let me in? You're
acting like a child.'

'No ...'

Her voice, for all her defiance, was scarcely loud enough
to carry, but the crash which followed came as alarming
as thunder to her ears. Damon had put a powerful
shoulder to the door and she stared, horrified, at the
smashed remains of the chair.

The door wasn't broken, though. Startled beyond words,
Tara watched him step coolly inside before closing and
locking it again. Then he pushed the key into his pyjama
pocket as if nothing out of the ordinary had happened.
Horror filled her at such convincing evidence of his
superior strength.

Casually he picked up the wrecked chair, placing it at
the other side of the room before carelessly dusting his
hands. 'Just one more thing you owe me for,' he mocked.

She would never say she was sorry, not if she lived to
be a thousand! 'Why have you come back?' she exclaimed,
shrinking against the pillows as he came towards her, standing over her and gazing down at her with a most satanic
look in his eyes.

Aloofly his brows rose. 'Why does a man usually come to
his bedroom at this time of night?' he asked suavely.

He wore, she saw, a pair of dark pyjamas under a short
silk dressing gown and her heart began beating as if it
was competing in a marathon race. 'You can't really be
serious about sleeping here?' she cried.

'Can't I?' he drawled harshly, staring at her closely,
as though impatient of the sheet she held so desperately
under her chin. 'I agree I could lock you in, but do you
think I would allow you the pleasure of escaping me by

climbing out of the window, as soon as I'd gone elsewhere?'

Anything to be rid of him! Her eyes were shadowed as she pleaded mutinously, 'You could lock that, as well.'

'I wouldn't put it past you to break it. There are no grilles outside to stop you and some of the creepers are as thick as a man's arm. You would be down in a flash, one way or another. I would either find you lying broken at the bottom or gone. Perhaps you would run for your French friend and his cabin cruiser, from which you could relay a message to Jonathan!'

'You know I wouldn't!' Tara sat still, her eyes fixed on his, wide with an indignation which left him unmoved.

'Yes, you would,' his dark eyes flashed, 'because you, like all your kind, have no conscience. You are never willing to take time to judge each case on its merits. Also it is true, is it not, that you find it difficult to believe I would ever foreclose on Tim?'

He turned away, as though there was no more to be said and disappeared into the bathroom. There Tara was forced to listen to him having a shower and to study her own inner reactions over sharing this room. How could she bear to lie here, only an arm's length away from where he would be peacefully sleeping. She hadn't ever seen him sleeping before. She had no doubt that he would sleep deeply but with the ability to awake at the slightest noise. If only she could get the key, she thought desperately, her nerves taut, even now, at the thought of slipping her hand into his pyjama jacket.

As he strolled back to the bedroom she noticed he was again wearing his silk pyjamas but had discarded the dressing gown. The pyjamas looked brand new, not in her honour, Tara felt sure. More likely it would be that usually he never wore any.

To hide her agitation, she said spitefully, 'Don't you wonder what the charming Miss Felton is going to think of this? Or is it perfectly allowable to have a little affair on the side in the circles you move in?'

His mouth tightened dangerously and he paused in the act of throwing back his bedcovers. 'Miss Felton won't know of this. They are on the other side of the house. Neither she nor Greg know where I'm sleeping.'

'I'll soon tell her!'

'You might be wiser not to, but this is up to you. Miss Felton would only believe it was the outpourings of a very jealous woman. No matter what I did she has more trust than you. Besides, she would never be convinced I could be interested in a plain young girl like you, not that way, no matter where I slept.'

'Such is her egoism, you mean, that she would never consider another woman a serious rival while she was around!' Such wild rage rose from his description of her that Tara didn't much care what she said. She felt hurt beyond what was normal, but his imperviousness was such she could never hope to hurt him back. 'Don't worry,' she jerked, between her teeth, 'I have no wish to even speak to her!'

'You will have to,' he said bluntly.

'Never!' There was some relief from pressure in the feeling she was able to put into that.

He ignored her defiance and she heard the mattress give beneath his weight as he got into bed. Settling himself calmly, he drew up a sheet negligently as he turned on his back, putting a hand behind his dark head. 'Finished with the light?' he asked.

'Yes!' she replied tautly, through the frantic pounding of her heart, which was reacting crazily to the sheer incredibility of the situation.

'Good!' His hand lifted and plunged the room into darkness. 'That's better,' he said.

Speechless, as her eyes grew accustomed to the grey gloom, she watched as he stretched his long legs contentedly under the sheet. Because he had thrown all the other bedclothes off, she could see his long, muscled outline too clearly. She drew a deep, shaken breath. 'I've never heard of anything so ridiculous as this!' she spluttered. 'I even feel that way.'

'You feel that way,' he drawled coolly, 'because you've never been married. The men who have taken you to bed have probably half mauled you before getting you there and in the morning, I imagine, they've usually been gone. You've obviously never been given time to study the male form—above or below the sheets.'

It was a minute before she could surface from cold shock. Her eyes were like green gems in her white face and she fancied he could see her consternation quite clearly and was enjoying it. She must ignore what he said. He would be waiting for her to deny she had ever slept with a man, but she wouldn't give him the satisfaction! Anyway, he wouldn't believe she was all that innocent, even if she protested until she was blue in the face. 'I don't understand?' she mocked, her voice admirably cool if a little too high. 'I never thought a Greek would ever go on like this!'

'I'm only half Greek, remember, and I've been around too much to belong wholly to the culture of any particular country. A man can very rarely make a fortune on his own doorstep, today. I suppose I'm a typical product of my kind,' he taunted, 'if you hadn't already guessed?'

'What you're trying to say,' she stared hard, hoping he could see her outrage, 'in fact what you're saying, is that men with money, your kind of money, are entitled to ignore the rules of decent society?'

She caught the impatience of his ironic sigh. 'I'm warning you, girl, don't provoke me! I'm all set to ignore the way I think you look in that fetching nightdress you're wearing. If you have any sense you won't weaken the little bit of resolve I have left.'

If she hadn't felt the way she did about him, Tara would have thrown herself on to the other bed and hit him, anything to relieve her increasing fright and resentment, but she dared not face the consequences should he retaliate. He was such a mixture of harsh passion and cool sophistication! Her fevered brain poured on. All muscles and powerful body, sheer masculine strength combined with aloof arrogance. 'Damn him,' she thought, 'damn him!' She wished she could have shouted it aloud and turned her words into stones as she did so, but a cowardly caution let her down. If she went on insulting him, his restraint, which she knew from experience was not unlimited, might break and, if he touched her, she wasn't sure what might happen. She might not be able to resist clinging to him, sobbing for clemency in his arms, and that she could never allow. Much better to wait until he slept, then think of something more effective than tears.

'Goodnight,' she said quietly, hoping the softness of her voice would deceive him into believing that at last she was beginning to do as she was told.

Turning on her side, she hoped he would think she was going to sleep. To further this impression she dragged a blanket around her shoulders and closed her eyes. If she had to wait for him to go to sleep, she would rather not see him. The less she saw of him the better. Once away from here she never wanted to see him again!

She had hoped time would pass very quickly; to her dismay it barely crawled. At last she became aware that Damon was beginning to turn over naturally, tossing from one side to another, then on his back, muttered a little like any normal person in the first throes of sleep. Opening her eyes slightly, she concentrated her gaze until she could just make out his face. One arm was thrown across it, the other hung loosely by his side, perfectly relaxed. Undoubtedly he was fast asleep.

Relief surging through her, Tara raised herself cautiously, glad of the release to her cramped muscles. Now she had to plan things out—something, she realised, she ought to have been doing this past half hour. Should she get out of bed and go right round the other side of him, or would it be wiser not to get out of bed at all but merely lean over the two feet dividing them and take the key this way, from Damon's pocket?

This way, if by some awful chance he woke, she could be out of bed and through the door before he had a chance of pulling himself together. Once outside the door could be locked and, if the others were as far away as he said they were, no one would hear him if he shouted. And she couldn't see him getting through the window!

Congratulating herself on the military-like precision of her strategy, Tara fixed the chair on which lay the borrowed blouse and shorts in her mind also. She could scarcely run to the taverna in what she had on. At the taverna she would arouse the Frenchman—whom she hadn't even thought of until Damon had mentioned him—and ask him to take her to the nearest large island.

The Frenchman had mentioned that he was ready to leave, she distinctly remembered him telling Veronica. He was older, but she didn't think he had lost his sense of adventure. She was sure he wouldn't mind obliging. Polos was isolated, but not that much. On another island, as soon as she reached it, she would catch a plane or steamer back to Athens and from there fly home. If she were lucky she might even get something direct, but she would never, she vowed, never tell Jonathan anything! One day—she stared, tears falling again, at Damon's sleeping face—he would realise she hadn't betrayed anybody and be sorry. In the meanwhile, it was better that she went quickly. This way she wouldn't be an embarrassment to Tim or anyone.

CHAPTER EIGHT

LULLED by the continuing quietness of Damon's breathing, Tara shifted carefully and stretched towards the other bed. Unfortunately, as she did so, he turned away from her on to his other side, so she could barely even touch him from where she was. The key would now be buried in his pocket against the mattress, quite out of reach from her present position.

'Damn—oh, damn!' she whispered under her breath again, not being able to remember when she had last felt at such odds with fate. Not knowing what to do she paused in momentary confusion. She could wait until he turned next time, but she was trembling so badly inside she knew she could never last out.

There was nothing for it, she must slip between the two beds and slide her hand over his back to reach the key. It was cowardly to stay here, just thinking about it. Trying to control the erratic throbbing of her pulses, she slid to the floor. It was a long reach and to be so near Damon had her senses reacting traitorously, but she forced herself not to waver. Then just as her fingers touched the key and were drawing it carefully from his pocket, other fingers—not her own—curled cruelly around her wrist. The terrible fright which hit her made her gasp and cry out.

'So!' His exclamation, as he raised himself on one elbow and gazed down on her, was full of cold amusement. 'Not a very accomplished thief, are you? Evidently much has been omitted from your training. I've known children with defter fingers than yours.'

'Let me go!' In vain she tried to tug her wrist from his grasp, almost screaming.

132

'Why should I?' his reply was brief, but the hand he laid on her head seemed to say much more. 'Maybe all you wanted was to be near me? Nearer than you were in your own bed?'

'Don't be ridiculous!' Tara jerked back as though stung, her face damp with perspiration, with fear and frustration. Her voice shaking, she half sobbed, as temper gave way suddenly to panic. 'Damon, please let me go! I know I've done wrong, trying to take the key, but if you'd been in my position, wouldn't you have tried something?'

'Maybe,' he conceded, his breath warm on her face, 'but I'd have used a little more sense! Do you think I was fooled, even for a minute? You never once moved. Only someone making devious plans could have lain as stiffly as you did.'

'At least I didn't pretend,' she gulped painfully. 'You seemed to be asleep while you must have been awake all the time!'

'Only because I suspected your every move, or maybe the ones you didn't make,' he jeered dryly, brushing his hand derisively over her tear-stained cheek, without any sign of being willing to let her go. He appeared to be deriving some distorted pleasure in allowing his lean fingers to explore the high cheekbones, the slight hollows beneath, the full, quivering curves of her mouth. 'You realise what you're inviting, coming so near me?' he murmured, his voice soft enough to make her shiver. 'You'd have been much wiser to have stayed where you were. You make it very difficult for a man to control his baser instincts. Maybe,' smoothly, 'you can understand what I'm talking about?'

'Don't be silly!' she gasped, attempting to disguise a quivering alarm. 'You exaggerate. I don't feel a thing!'

'Convince me, then!' he muttered thickly, pulling her quickly down to him. 'I don't know what you really think of me, but at least I'm convinced you're not altogether indifferent. You're very attractive,' his eyes searched through the darkness to find the beautiful curves of her slender body, 'I don't see why I shouldn't consider my own comfort for a change.'

'No—don't!' she groaned, but closed her eyes as he bent his head and the biting pressure of his mouth both hurt and excited her. Too late she realised the trap set by her own senses. His fingers laced through her hair as he twisted her ruthlessly to the pillows, and when his head bent and his lips caressed her bare shoulder, the already warm blood in her veins seemed to turn to fire.

'Come. I want you beside me,' he commanded, his eyes glittering darkly as he raised his head to stare at her.

Even had she wished, Tara didn't think she could have moved. And, in spite of the turmoil within her, she still had a desire to fight him.

As if impatiently aware of this, he didn't ask her twice. His arms went completely around her and he lifted her on to the bed. 'Now,' he rasped savagely, 'we might see what sort of woman you really are.'

Not giving her another opportunity to protest, he turned up her averted chin, his mouth finding hers with a force which sent tremors all the way down her slight body. Before she could prevent it he had brushed her fragile nightgown aside, his hand closing possessively over her throbbing breast.

'Damon!' she cried, pushing against him, shocked, as she wrenched her mouth away, at the strange emotions sweeping through her. 'You must let me go!'

'Not now. You had it coming!' Then, more roughly, 'Don't turn away. I need you——!'

His mouth, when it again captured hers, tasted of wine and she felt weak, too weak to go on fighting him. She no longer seemed to care whether it was torture or ecstasy as she clung to him helplessly. Surrendering to the magnetism of him, her fingers curled in his thick hair, pressing his mouth urgently closer. His hands slid to her hips, pulling her fiercely to him. Responding involuntarily, her lips parted under his, with an eagerness she could no longer hide.

'Tara ...' She heard him murmuring her name, several times, as his body moved hungrily. His voice was harsh but there was a sudden depth to it she hadn't heard before. She couldn't answer and as his hands moulded and explored she was lost in an abandonment of increasing delight. No longer was she conscious of what she was doing, or of where she was. Feverishly she moaned against the pressure of his mouth, her limbs, crushed under his, aching with a longing he seemed deliberately to increase, with every experienced movement of his hands and strong body. She was dizzy and had no coherent thought left in her head, only a whirlwind of mindless desire.

Afterwards, she thought she had never known such shock as when his arms suddenly left her. In a flash, it seemed, she was suddenly lying alone on a bed where only moments ago he had been holding her as though he would liked to have kept her there with him for ever. 'Damon?' she whispered, her arms going out, unconsciously groping for him, wanting him back. He couldn't leave her like this!

He didn't, or he pretended he didn't hear. Later, she thought she should perhaps have been grateful that he didn't switch on the light, so that the darkness covered her first anguish. Not immediately would her senses accept he had gone. 'Damon?' she murmured, her voice more entreating than she knew.

'Go to sleep,' was all the reply she got, and then harshly.

'Sleep?' she breathed dazedly, pausing as her bewildered mind marvelled at the word. 'But—Damon ...?'

'Be quiet!' he retorted brusquely, bending to retrieve his pyjamas from the floor, between the two beds.

'Oh!' As she realised what he was doing, reaction began hitting her unmercifully.

'See what you've escaped?' There was no pity in the dry query, merely a hardening contempt, an awful jeering.

'But, Damon, why?' It seemed a question she had to ask.

It looked at first as if he wasn't going to answer, for all her unhappiness must have reached him quite clearly. Then he said tautly, 'You've never been so near a man before, despite my former suspicions, and I find I don't wish for the possible complications of getting involved with a girl like you. You could become a clinging vine I wouldn't know what to do with, and at the moment I have other, more urgent commitments.'

'Another woman?'

'Yes.'

How emphatic he sounded, how brutally detached. Tara's heart felt like lead, misery smote her heavily. 'Angela?'

'Maybe.'

Bitterly Tara groped for the covering comfort of a blanket, glad suddenly that all feeling seemed to be leaving her. 'I feel ashamed,' she choked, 'of both myself—and you.'

'Really?' he mocked tightly.

'I don't know how I could have acted the way I did,' she was deaf to his cool taunt, 'nor do I understand how you can be so determined to steal another man's fiancée!'

'You don't understand much, do you, Tara?' There was a terse savageness in his voice, speaking of a much tried patience. 'At the moment you're not liking me very much,, but you might have reason later, when the right man comes along, to be thankful I am able to exert restraint, no matter how difficult. Haven't I just shown you the danger in—certain situations?'

But paradise, too, she wanted to cry, while knowing she couldn't. He didn't want her. Not that she wanted him to want her now! As he had said, she had learnt a valuable lesson. How had she ever imagined she loved him? Too mixed up to think rationally, Tara closed her eyes tightly against the sensuous recollection of his experienced lovemaking—clenching her fists just as fiercely in order to consolidate her defences.

'Go to sleep, Tara,' she heard him advising, through the taut silence she could almost feel. He added grimly, in a low voice, as if the admission was dragged out of him, 'You're not the only one who'd give anything to be able to seek another room. This wasn't the best of ideas, but you didn't give it a chance. If you'd conducted yourself in a reasonable manner we might both have been feeling more comfortable. After you go to sleep I intend working for the rest of the night. I have some papers with me.'

'Nice for you!' she retorted acidly, hiding her face in her arms against the pillows, for fear he should notice her body beginning to shake with sobs.

In the morning she couldn't remember when she had at last fallen asleep. Sheer exhaustion must, in the end, have induced a restless slumber. Thankfully she saw, when she awoke, that the other twin bed was empty, as was the room. Putting suddenly shaky legs to the floor, she stared nervously towards the bathroom door before deciding to risk it. To her relief the bathroom was empty, too. There was no sign of the tall, grim Greek anywhere. Tara sighed, brushing a trembling hand over heavy eyes, wishing that the events of the past hours might just have been the bad dream they seemed this morning.

Showering quickly, she reluctantly donned the silk blouse and shorts, aware that her evening dress would only seem ridiculous. Not that she minded that so much, but in shorts she might make better use of any opportunity to escape. Both garments, though too big, made her blush. The blouse was so thin it revealed far too much and the shorts barely reached the top of her long, slender legs. Angela Felton must be all set on a seduction course if she made a habit of wearing clothes like these. In vain Tara looked around for something she might use to cover up, but not even a closer inspection of the huge wardrobes in the room produced anything she could wear. There seemed nothing for it but to venture downstairs as she was.

For the first time it struck her that the door might still be locked, but when she rushed across the room and tried it, to her relief it opened as she turned the knob.

On going downstairs she was surprised to find Angela and Damon in the hall. They were standing close together, and intuitively Tara knew, with a horribly familiar feeling in her heart, they had been kissing each other. Over Angela's shoulder she fancied his face paled as he encountered the contemptuous look she gave him.

'Good morning,' he said coldly, and she wondered if his cold tone was for Angela's sake or because he genuinely didn't like her. Against her will Tara found herself recalling other mornings when his welcome had been warmer. Those idyllic days on his boat, when even the battles of words they had regularly engaged in had not been able to destroy a kind of fundamental rapport between them. Hollowly, Tara admitted now it could never have been like that at all!

'Good morning,' she replied, lowering her gaze to the floor, but managing an indifferent shrug of tense shoulders before looking up again.

Angela didn't speak, only nodded coolly, her eyes mocking the ill fit of Tara's shorts. Damon's stare, Tara noticed, was keener, going over her deliberately, reminding her how persistent his hands and mouth had been. Which was a crazy thing to think of, she told herself sharply. It wouldn't do any good now.

'We're just going in to breakfast,' Damon's mouth curled at the corners, as if he knew exactly what was on her mind. 'You will join us, of course.'

About to say she wasn't hungry, Tara realised she must have at least a cup of coffee. She would never be able to look after herself if her inner resources were weakened for want of food. Not that she felt like eating anything, but she was thirsty. As for joining them, she doubted if she would be allowed any choice.

'Thank you,' she murmured, adding with frigid politeness, 'I hope your brother is feeling better this morning?'

'He is still sleeping,' Damon answered abruptly. 'I'm afraid he's had a bad night.'

Angela said sharply as they sat down, 'I really think, Damon darling, he should seek further advice about his nerves.'

Damon glanced at her with patient dryness. 'I don't think there is anyone left to consult. They all seem to believe his nervous system is something he'll have to learn to live with—and this will, unfortunately, include you, of course. However,' he added, with a slight smile, 'as it might only involve long periods of relaxation in quiet places like this it won't be so very terrible. In the end the worst that could probably happen would be a change in his career.'

As Angela's eyes widened and she frowned, Tara saw Damon, who was sitting very close to her, lay a hand on her arm, as if sensing she was in need of comfort.

'Don't worry, Angela,' he said softly, 'I could, if necessary, find him something with me. He's always been keen on shipping.'

'But you own everything!'

'Not everything!' he retorted enigmatically, and Tara went cold as she watched his eyes wander over Angela with what to her appeared undisguised longing in their depths. 'He does have certain—assets I don't have. It might have served him better if we'd both shared the same father, but I promise to do my best for him. I'm sure he could hold down some sort of position.'

'But you don't think it will come to having to give up his present career?'

Damon hesitated. 'I couldn't honestly say, Angela. You must know his agent better than I do, but the last chat I had with the fellow wasn't very promising. It was confidential, naturally, and the man was obviously a bit strung up after Greg disappeared.'

Angela's eyes hardened as she stared down at her small glass of orange juice, as though she was dismissing a problem. Tara noticed her face clearing, her mind plainly made up about something. Her thin mouth softening in a glorious smile, she turned again to Damon. 'You're so kind, darling. I wish—oh well, it doesn't matter.'

Tara stared, in dazed fascination, a terrible churning in her stomach, as Angela suddenly reached across tenderly to place a warm kiss on Damon's cheek. As he turned quickly, his lips caught her mouth. Tara was sure it had been a deliberate manoeuvre on his part. 'So very kind,' Angela purred again.

'You're very lovely, so easy to be kind to,' he continued, looking at her intently, taking no notice of Tara whatsoever.

'Be careful, Damon darling.' Angela, who Tara sensed would never allow emotion to carry her away, stared triumphantly over the table. 'We mustn't give our little friend from the press something more to put in her scandal column.

'You mustn't think me stupid,' Damon glanced at Tara derisively. 'You don't think I'd be talking this way if I hadn't got our little friend—exactly where I wanted her? And that's in no position to say anything at all!'

Instantly, before she could stop herself, Tara was on her feet, her face burning, then starkly white. How could Damon sit there, making love to another man's fiancée, in broad daylight? It was unforgivable, too, that he was murmuring the same endearments to Angela as he had to her. So well Tara recalled how he had assured her she was beautiful. Gullible, would have been nearer the mark, she thought savagely. How easily men prattled out such flattery! How utterly foolish women were in believing them!

Across the space which divided them, her shocked eyes

met Damon's and she hoped her glance was as cold as she
felt. Snatching up her cup of coffee, she muttered something about having it in the sunshine as she hurried from
the room. She was determined to spare herself the embarrassment of having to watch them and she didn't stop to
ask herself, if it had been anyone else but Damon Voulgaris, if it would have mattered.

As she left she heard Angela ask coldly, 'Is it really
necessary to have that girl around, darling?'

And Damon's heart-shaking reply, 'I'd rather not risk
her being free to summon a horde of newshounds here, my
dear, not until we have something more to tell them.'

Tara, striving desperately to control a sudden trembling
in order not to spill her coffee, tried to concentrate on her
surroundings, rather than the two she had left behind.
Last night everything had seemed blurred, and on her
secret expedition the day before she had only seen the outer
walls of the villa and the gardens. Now she saw the interior,
the long, low rooms of the ground floor, the polished old
mahogany, the deep-silled windows which betrayed the
depth of the white walls. All around were set glowing
pieces of glass and china, beautiful carved ivories, yellow
with age, fine old glass, glowing with many colours,
jewelled ikons, brilliant pottery, tiny gilded statuettes of
saints. Gazing spellbound, momentarily jerked from her
unhappiness, Tara felt enchanted, wishing she might have
known the history of each enchanting piece. Someone had
obviously selected and collected with loving care and a
wealth of near professional knowledge of such things, as
well as a great appreciation. As a collection, many of the
pieces must be worth a small fortune and she wondered
that Damon wasn't frightened of losing them. Surely it
would be only too easy for thieves to break in and steal
and pillage?

Damon made no attempt to follow her and the house,
apart from a few soft-footed servants, seemed deserted.
Thoughtfully drinking her coffee, Tara, after another

quick look around, forced herself to abandon such treasures and wander outside.

It was autumn, but the sun and air were still warm. The villa inside was cool, the light shadowed. Here it was bright and clear, with a wonderful radiance. Heavily scented jasmine still bloomed against the long terraces, masses of bougainvillea cascaded over white walls and framed arches. Climbing geranium and heliotrope, planted in huge tubs, decorated pillars and black cypresses and other hedging made a striking background for still colourful borders. The air was filled with a thousand scents, those of the garden blending insidiously with the sharper tang of the higher, distant pines and the rosemary and thyme of the lower valleys. The beauty of it all caught at Tara's sore heart and, if it failed to soothe entirely, at least she wasn't indifferent to its enchantment.

Yet all the time she stood and gazed her mind was already working on something else. Damon hadn't followed her. Could this mean he was giving her the opportunity to escape? Perhaps he had realised the folly of keeping her a prisoner, the embarrassment, too, should she happen to say anything to Angela about last night.

Carefully putting down the coffee cup she had unthinkingly carried out with her, Tara took a closer look round. Not until she did this did she notice the two men standing, half hidden, at the end of one of the terraces. Frowning, she tried not to give the impression of staring, but she could have sworn she had seen the same men aboard Damon's yacht. They were obviously not guests, so they must be guards. Perhaps not even professionally that. They might be here entirely for her benefit, to see she didn't escape. Anger flared inside her. All the time she had been planning so carefully, how he must have been laughing at her! Making idle love to Angela in the dining room and amusing himself quietly at the thought of Tara standing here, thinking she had nothing else to do but walk out.

Her suspicions seemed well founded when, seconds later, she heard him behind her. 'You weren't thinking of trying to get away?'

Furiously she swung around, glad for once of her quick temper which could hide, among other things, a growing despair. 'A lot of chance I'd have had,' she cried sharply, 'seeing how you appear to employ an army of bodyguards!'

'Oh, they're scarcely that,' he replied lightly, 'but they are well able to serve that purpose. Don't you think I'm wise,' he taunted, as her lips curled, 'to ensure the safety and privacy of those of whom I'm fond?'

'Don't you think this absurd state of affairs has gone on long enough?' she countered. 'I refuse to stay here and be forced to watch while you practically steal your brother's fiancée from under his very nose.'

'I knew her first,' Damon said coldly.

'You knew her first!' Tara repeated blankly, her eyes widening with amazement as they met his. She was aware of pain but also of another bewildering impression, that he was trying to tell her something. She paused and her eyes flickered, but the feeling was smothered by equally bewildering ones. If Damon Voulgaris really wanted a woman she couldn't imagine her getting away from him, but if Damon hadn't wanted Angela, when he had apparently had the chance, why did he want her now? However uncertain she might be about him in many ways, Tara was sure he was, above all things, a man who would know his own mind.

'Does this surprise you?' he asked, arrogantly, she thought.

'Not really,' she said, frowning slowly. 'I'm only surprised that she deserted you for Greg. I mean,' she stammered, suddenly horrified to realise she had spoken her thoughts aloud and searching desperately to improvise at the sight of his sardonically raised brows, 'what I'm trying to point out is that she appears extremely fond of you.'

'You've noticed?'

Tara trembled, but her eyes met his with spirit. 'I'd have to be blind not to.'

'But you should learn, should you not, not to take everything you see at face value.'

Once more she had the uncanny feeling he was trying to tell her something, but, she decided, meeting the ironic glint in his eye, it could be nothing she would welcome learning. It was more likely he was attempting to tell her, without words, that his kisses last night—in case she had other ideas—meant nothing. The colour left Tara's already pale face as she remembered her own passionate response, a response that she felt terrified, if repeated, might eventually betray her.

She drew a deep breath. 'Mr Voulgaris, I don't want to remain here to see—anything!'

He stiffened but gave no sign that her words, her tormented expression, worried him emotionally. 'We won't go through all that again. You will stay for as long as I deem it necessary.'

'If you refuse to let me go,' she said hoarsely, making sure Angela hadn't followed Damon out, 'I won't spend another night like the last!'

His mouth twisted with mocking derision. 'What exactly are you complaining of?'

'I think you're despicable!' she gasped, aware of the knowledge in him which allowed him to taunt her so. He would, she knew with a kind of hollow despair, have been able to assess much of what she'd tried to hide, from the way she had clung to him passionately. It was up to her to make it clear that such a momentary weakness would not be repeated. 'I refuse . . .' she began again.

Before the sentence was half out his hands caught her savagely by the shoulders, dragging her to him so she was almost swamped by his hard, masculine strength. Through his half open shirt she had a near suffocating view of his broad, hair-covered chest, the same chest from which near contact had left scratches on her own this morning. Her heart sank, then raced as he said curtly, 'Listen to me, Tara! While you're here you'll do exactly as you're told. I don't wish to hear you say refuse to me again! As for tonight, if we are to look that far ahead, you will certainly sleep alone, even though,' he jeered, 'you may come to regret it. I have so much work to get through I doubt if I will get to bed at all.'

'You worked last night,' she retorted, unthinkingly.

'Work?' His voice was grim.

Her eyes dared no further than the jutting line of his jaw, the hard, wide curves of his sensuous mouth. Her throat was dry and she had to swallow twice before she could speak. 'You said you were going to put on the light as you had work to do.'

He laughed mirthlessly, as she reminded him. 'Do you think I got through any, girl, with you lying next to me, weeping under the bedclothes!'

'If I was,' she gasped, horrified he had noticed, 'it was only because you'd made me angry.'

'That, and other things.' He wasn't easily deceived.

'Oh!' In sobbing fury, Tara hit out at him, only to find her flying fists imprisoned in one large hand, while his other tightened around her back to crush her against him.

'One day,' he said, through clamped teeth, 'you'll learn to stop fighting me. Until then I can only demonstrate how you are wasting your time.'

His body was hard, to be near it brought tormenting memories. Tara felt shaken with relief when he put her abruptly from him. 'Learn to behave yourself,' he held her a second until she regained her balance and colour. 'You are to stay here and must make the best of it. You won't come to any harm, but I want no more remarks about Miss Felton. Now we go swimming.'

'In the pool?' Tara felt too shaky to make any remarks about anything else, and she must lick her wounds later, when there was no one to see.

'No.' His eyes narrowed as he saw how she bit her lip to stop it trembling, but he only said, 'We'll go down to the beach. There is more freedom there. The pool is too tame for me this morning.'

Unhappily Tara sensed the frustration still in him. Naturally this would be so, until he succeeded in breaking his brother's engagement. Bitterly she exclaimed, 'I'd rather not join you, Mr Voulgaris.'

'You have no choice,' he said briefly, taking no notice of her return to the use of his surname. 'Angela will again lend you something to wear and Greg will join us.'

'I must stay near the house. Tim might get in touch.'

Damon looked at her steadily. 'I've already talked to him. He won't be ringing again today.'

'But there's something I want to speak to him about!' She stared at him, her protesting cry falling, she realised, on deaf ears as he turned away.

'Be ready,' was all he said, and she knew she must be content.

In spite of Damon giving the impression that they were about to leave immediately, it was after eleven before anyone seemed ready to go. Damon was apparently busy in his study and when Angela wandered from the house later she said they were waiting for Greg to come down. Aloofly she handed Tara a green swimsuit which Tara went to put on under her shorts.

When she came back Angela wondered tartly, 'I can't think why Damon wants you to join us. His men would be more than willing to look after someone like you.'

The blood seemed to chill in Tara's veins as she met the cold stare trained so vindictively on her. It struck her that Angela Felton could be a dangerous person to cross. Angela wouldn't care what happened to someone she didn't like, so long as she got rid of them. Damon might have his faults, but surely he wouldn't do anything like this! 'He wouldn't dare hand me over to them,' she choked, yet felt suddenly frightened, not sure of anything or anyone any more.

'There's not much he won't do if sufficiently provoked,' Angela assured her, her superior manner proclaiming such a comprehensive knowledge of her subject that Tara felt unconsciously miserable again. 'A girl like you,' Angela added cuttingly, 'wouldn't stand a chance.'

With a flair for acting which rather shocked her, Tara observed sweetly, 'How thankful you must be for Greg, who must be much easier to manage as well as being famous.'

'But not so exciting.' Angela paused with studied innocence. 'What a story for your newspaper, Miss Curtis, if Greg and I were to part and I became engaged to Damon.'

Damon's voice came echoing back—'I knew her first.' Tara's lips felt frozen, too cold to move as Angela continued slowly, 'I believe Damon is convinced I've made a mistake.'

Bitterly, Tara said, 'How nice to be able to pick and choose! You appear to enjoy famous men, Miss Felton. Of course your father is very well known.'

'Well known and rich. I would never need to marry for money,' Angela smiled smugly, as though for once Tara had pleased her. 'It just so happens that the most exciting men are often wealthy. Take Damon, for instance. Sometimes just to look at him is enough to make me realise I could never let him go.'

'Do you—love him?' Tara was scarcely conscious of how she faltered, or of how terrible she felt.

'Love!' Angela gave a hoot of brittle laughter. 'That's something I never think about. What I want from a man, my dear, isn't love, or even sex. It's simply the sort of background I'm used to. If he happens also to possess the kind of good looks which make other women green with envy, then so much the better. It's just young girls like yourself who are foolish enough to get enmeshed in love.'

Feeling too sick to even try to think of an answer, Tara was glad to see Damon and Greg coming up behind them, although she hoped, in dismay, that Greg, at least, hadn't overheard what Angela had been saying. She noticed Greg didn't so much as bother to kiss his fiancée good morning, and while it was possible Angela had already seen him in his bedroom, Tara didn't think Angela would be the bedroom visiting kind.

Tara could see Greg still looked harassed and felt unhappy because of his sulky, little-boy look as he glanced at her. She could well believe it true what Damon had said about Greg's nerves being bad.

Angela, as if not caring to be even near him, took Damon's arm and led the way down to the shore. Expecting Greg to follow silently, Tara was startled to hear him apologising for his rude behaviour the night before.

'I'm sorry,' he frowned wryly. 'Supposing you really are a newspaper reporter, it was no excuse. I can see now you're just a sweet kid.'

'Your brother doesn't appear to think so!'

Greg's frown deepened. 'I know. I've been trying to work it out. He's not usually so intolerant. I'm the one, more often than not, without patience. It must be because you're from the press.'

'But I'm not! That's what he refuses to believe.'

'It's mostly because of your brother in the U.K.' Greg sighed ruefully. 'Unfortunately he's on the staff of a well known newspaper and you did promise to help him. This is why Damon won't let you go. He can't bear to think he's been deceived, but it won't really matter in a day or two.'

'Why not?' Tara knew she sounded painfully eager, but Greg's sudden friendliness was so warming she forgot about caution. 'Are you leaving—and what about Miss Felton?'

Greg's sudden friendliness rapidly dispersed, although he stared with quickening interest at Tara's more animated face. 'There you go again, asking too many questions. If you're out to convince Damon of your innocence, I shouldn't let him hear you.'

What a strange, unpredictable lot they were! Tara shivered at Greg's sharper tones. To look at, Greg was nothing like his half-brother. He was tall, but there the resemblance ended as he was much slimmer and fairer, yet they both shared the same caustic tongue. 'I don't mind if Damon does hear me,' she replied shortly. 'And I certainly don't feel a need to convince him of anything. Your brother doesn't like me, Mr Golden, so he's only too ready to believe the worst.'

'He may not like you,' Greg scoffed, 'but I happen to have seen the way he looks at you. Maybe desire might be more apt. I'm surprised he even allows you to walk with me. Damon is half Greek, you know. More than just half, in many ways, when it comes to getting what he wants, especially if it's a woman.'

Hurt flared. Greg could be just as hateful as Damon, but Damon would never be so blind. Surely Greg didn't enjoy seeing Damon and his fiancée standing so close together? There was scarcely more than an inch or two between them as they stood talking at the water's edge. Angela's face was smiling as she gazed up into Damon's eyes and, even as Tara and Greg approached, she reached up and kissed him.

Tartly, because she felt so terrible, Tara exclaimed, 'There are some women whom Damon doesn't appear to have to fight very hard to get!'

CHAPTER NINE

THE sea was warm with lazy waves lapping the shore and so blue as to be dazzling, yet overall lay a certain hint of wilder autumn days to come. Tara shivered as she dipped an exploratory toe into the water. She wasn't cold, but the picture of Damon and Angela so close to each other stayed with her. He hadn't done anything to avoid Angela's tantalising lips and, even now, while gazing towards the distant horizon, Tara could still see them. Greg had simply shrugged and walked away. Feverishly Tara wished she could have shared his cool indifference.

The swimsuit Angela had loaned her suffered the same fault as the shorts and blouse, but it was a one-piece and easily adjustable. With a length of string she had picked up tied around her narrow waist and the halter neck tightened, Tara saw it covered her almost completely. It might not be very flattering, but it felt safe. She didn't realise how the colour of it suited her, how it accentuated the gem-like glow of her huge eyes and brought a touch of almond to the fairness of her burnished hair.

Taking a deep breath, she wandered over to Damon, managing to ask coolly, her glance unconsciously challenging, 'Am I allowed to swim where I like?'

'Not exactly.' His eyes went lazily over her, appearing to pinpoint attractions she had thought well covered. 'Stay within a hundred yards of the shore. You'll notice my yacht out there. My men have instructions to keep an eye on my guests, for their own safety, of course.'

Startled, she swung her head, her eyes exploring the bay. Sure enough, at the far side of it, against a backdrop of high cliffs and deep foliage, the splendid white yacht rode at anchor. Tara hadn't noticed it. So far as she could see there were no men lining the decks, but somehow she didn't doubt Damon's word. It was quite obvious, from the cold set of his face as he continued to stare at her, he didn't intend she should escape.

Forgetting that Angela was beside them, Tara cried angrily, 'You really are putting yourself out for your brother, aren't you? I find it difficult to believe there's no self-interest somewhere!'

Taking no notice of his sharp, short reply, she turned from him, splashing clumsily until the water grew deep enough to dive straight into the sea. Let him curse and rant as much as he liked, she thought fiercely, squashing down a niggling apprehension as she determined to call his bluff. She had a sudden conviction he wouldn't do anything much if she did try to get away.

Keeping parallel with the shore she swam strongly, as if seeking relief from her tormenting unhappiness in physical exhaustion. The bay was private, enclosed by high cliffs, but around the next corner, if she were clever enough to get there before anyone saw her, there might be no cliffs at all. She might, if lucky, find an easy path back to the taverna. It hadn't seemed so very far the other day. Once at the taverna she was sure, if she promised not to contact Jonathan, Damon would allow her to remain. Whatever happened she couldn't imagine him dragging her out by the hair of her head, screaming, with an audience of villagers. 'He must let me stay!' she whispered aloud. She couldn't bear to stop where she was, forced to watch him making love to Angela, practically stealing his half-brother's fiancée!

Wishing to confuse anyone who might be watching, Tara began making little dives, then swimming back in circles. Then, diving again, she swam swiftly under water in the direction of the next bay. This was something she had been good at and, though lack of practice hampered her a little, she still had a good turn of speed. To her relieved delight, when she surfaced, she had reached her destination and a few urgent strokes brought her rapidly inshore.

Counting on Damon being too engrossed with Angela, as soon as her feet touched the bottom she began racing towards the sheltering rocks. They weren't very high and, as she had hoped, there were plenty of tracks between them leading to the scrub and tree-covered waste-land beyond. So much for Damon Voulgaris and his flotilla of watch-dogs! she sniffed.

Then, to her horror, as she glanced anxiously over her shoulder, like a Greek god of old, rising from the sea, she saw Damon coming from the water. He wasn't all that far behind. What a fool she had been to think he wouldn't notice she was missing! She paused, thunderstruck, the whole of her filled with horrified alarm as he brushed the wet hair from his eyes and threw his head back. His long legs planted firmly apart on the sand, he stood shading his eyes with his hand, until he found her. It wasn't until then that Tara began to flee.

She had the advantage of him, she kept assuring herself as she ran, but on the top of the rise of land above the shore she knew she wasn't going to make it. She could still run, with the same graceful, fleeting movement of a young deer. Unfortunately she had forgotten the necessity of bringing shoes and her feet were being slowly cut to ribbons. 'Fool, fool, fool!' she heard herself muttering in hysterical self-condemnation as she winced with pain.

Behind her she could hear, also, Damon crashing after her and was aware she must stop. There was nothing else for it but to try and bluff her way out. She turned to face him, her throat so dry and tight she was foolishly tempted to put out her tongue and catch a dribble of the water which was still dripping from her hair. For a second she closed her eyes, as though to cancel the sight and sound of him, but it did nothing to make him disappear.

When she looked again she saw he was savagely angry, a livid monster, clothed as lightly as she. He covered the last yards between them with a few swift strides, his eyes holding her frustrated ones contemptuously.

'You may well look on me as Hades, or one of his brothers,' he exclaimed grimly, only the deep rise and fall of his bare chest betraying that his breathing had quickened with exertion.

There was a long pause while Tara listened to her own sobbing breath. Torn between tears and angry defiance, she let the latter win. Tears, she suspected, in Damon's present frame of mind, would have little effect. 'There's no need to get in such a state!' she cried sharply. 'I was only seeking a bit of privacy.'

'Don't give me that!' he gritted between his teeth.

Tara's courage began to vanish and she felt herself attacked by great tremors, which weren't caused by cold. The air around them was warm and still, the sun hot through the shady branches above their head. Damon was furious, she could read it in the set of his mouth, the glitter in his eyes, eyes which were cold enough to chill her. She had transgressed, he considered she had betrayed his trust, and she had no means of avoiding whatever punishment he was devising.

It might be a waste of time to try avoiding it, but try she must. She had an uneasy feeling it would be quicker to pretend to be a young boy, to pick up a stick and hand it to him as she bent over. Then justice could be dispensed swiftly and done with. Nervously she wondered what he had in mind.

'I'm sorry,' she said, 'if you are annoyed, but it was your own fault.'

'Explain yourself!'

If only, Tara wished desperately, he would be kinder, but perhaps he was giving her a chance. Trying to hold on to any little ground she might have gained, she rested aggressive fists on her thighs and changed an anxious glance into a glare. 'I wasn't going to stay and watch you flirting with Angela Felton any longer! You're nothing but a liar and a cheat, Damon Voulgaris, and if you don't let me go I'm going to tell Angela how many times you've kissed me. It might be one way of convincing her she could be much better with the man she's already engaged to!'

'Will you shut up!' His face was white under his tan, but she knew it was from anger. A man like this would never feel ashamed of himself. None the less, she was too frightened of the dark glitter about him to do anything else but obey. 'You're more foolhardy than I thought,' he said grimly, 'if you dare threaten me.'

She stared at him, anxiety and tiredness making her eyes huge. His hands had descended on her bare shoulders, gripping so fiercely she feared the imprint of his fingers might remain for ever. As she watched his mouth twist harshly a wild sense of alarm went swiftly through her, shaking the slender contours of her shrinking body. Yet stubbornly she gasped, 'You're a fine one to talk! You've done nothing but threaten me—ever since we met.'

'With good reason,' his eyes narrowed in savage violence. 'Someone has to look after a girl as reckless as you. Didn't you realise there are tricky currents around the rocks out there? You could have been swept out to sea.'

'Then you would have been well rid of me, as everyone else appears to be as blind as Greg!'

A muscle jerked at the side of his mouth and his eyes were so brilliant with anger that involuntarily she shrank. One moment his control was gone, the next it was there again, but held only with difficulty. 'We'll stick to your indiscretions,' he snarled curtly, 'not mine.'

Again his dark glance went over her, seeing how her swimsuit seemed to have broken loose from its moorings and hung drunkenly about her salt-hazed curves. She wasn't to know she looked extraordinarily beautiful, with her fine bones and muted colouring, which made such an intriguing and tantalising background for her wonderful sea-green eyes. 'Did you intend returning to the taverna like this?'

His voice was harsh, as if he were considering his own

reactions to that question more than hers. There was in him some silent rage which made her pulse race afresh and forced her to endure his intimate inspection. 'Why not?' she pushed the words through taut lips. 'I'm English, remember?'

'Yes,' he retorted tightly, as she tossed her damp head and tried to wriggle from his hands, 'I know nicely what you are. One of these days, when I have more time ...'

'But that won't ever be, will it?' Because she couldn't escape his grip and from it she seemed to have stirred living flames which proceeded to sweep through her, she interrupted him rebelliously, 'You're much too busy with the wonderful Miss Felton. No wonder you wanted to keep out the press!'

'I won't warn you again to shut up!'

'Why should I?'

'There's one way I can make you.'

'No!' The sarcasm in his voice and her own belated instincts warned her where her wilfulness was leading, and she panicked. She didn't want to be in his arms, to feel his mouth on hers. In other circumstances, she was ashamed to admit, she might have given anything for even a few seconds of such rapture, but not when he was angry. Then the kisses he dispensed were something she would rather not think about. Nervously she threw back her head, daring to look straight at him. 'No, Damon, what you have in mind won't solve anything.'

'I agree.' A little of his anger faded but his voice was still thick with vengeful intent, 'and it only builds up tension of a different kind, but with you it seems the only reprisal I can think of. If it maddened me to see you trying to escape, regardless of my warnings, at least you've given me an excuse to have you in my arms.'

He lowered his head and she stopped trying to fight him. It was useless to even attempt it. Besides, she didn't know that she even wanted to. As his mouth found hers his arms went swiftly around her body, firm on her bare flesh as he drew her close. Because he wore only swimming trunks of the briefest nature, she could actually feel the powerful beat of his heart thundering against the breathless race of her own, as she suddenly clung to him. Her mouth crushed under his, she felt the same urgent desire which seemed to be motivating him. His hand left her hip to close about her nape, holding her head steady under his probing mouth. His expertise was brilliant, bringing her instantly to a wild surrender. If this was loving and being loved, she would have liked it to have gone on for ever!

She was half lying against him, her balance gone, just yearning that this incredible, drowning excitement might continue. The masculine scent of him, the warmth of his skin, which tensed to hard muscle where her fevered fingers clutched, moved her to a kind of desperation. She had thought she had had enough of him last night, but she knew now this wasn't true. His drugged kisses had her floating and she didn't know the exact moment he picked her up and carried her deeper under the shadows of the tree that sheltered them.

As he laid her on the ground her hair fell across her cheek and he brushed it aside, murmuring something she was beyond hearing as he did so. She was deaf and blind to everything but the feel of him, the overwhelming passion he was arousing. A wild tremor shook her as she caught a glimpse of his chiselled features, the strong jaw and determined mouth, the virile attraction which drew her so surely.

As he came down beside her, his hand thrust her swimsuit aside to find her breasts and the pressure of his mouth deepened into a hungry urgency. Tara floundered, gasping, as if she had been in the sea she had just left, but instead of water it was fire which swept her away. As Damon's arms tightened she whirled, burning up in the flames of his merciless desire. All she wanted was to get nearer, so they might, the flames and the darkness, have their way with her.

It came almost like a physical blow when he lifted his head, jerking tensely against the pressure of her ardently entwined arms around his neck.

'Tara!'

His voice sounded slightly unsteady, but clipped, as though he sought to control it. His hands moved from the more vulnerable parts of her body, back to her shoulders to hold her motionless as he stared down at her. In the half light she lay trembling, her mouth burning. Only partly conscious, she wanted to move, before he could read everything he wanted from the betraying emotion on her yearning face. So many different feelings consumed her she scarcely knew herself any more. There was only one thing she could fix on with any certainty. If this man went, despite his cruelty, her reason for living might easily go with him.

'Tara!' He spoke again and her eyes opened reluctantly.

For a long moment they stared at each other and she read in his a self-denial which sobered her ruthlessly. It was like a blow, but it helped her resist the magnetism which, even now, pulled her back to him. Her lips parted, throbbing, and as she bent her head to adjust the strap of her swimsuit with fumbling fingers, her hair spilled wildly about her flushed face.

As he drew her gently up beside him, her hands weren't nearly as dexterous as his had been. With a heavy sigh he finished the task, but not before his eyes had taken one last look at her.

Urgently she whispered, closing her eyes again, feeling everything might be sacrificed without regret for a few more hours in Damon's arms. What comfort would pride and her chastity bring her in the years to come, the long, lonely years without him? 'Darling,' she breathed, her voice low and halting, 'I'm in no hurry to go back if you aren't.'

She heard his breath rasp, saw the strength of his throat tense so the veins stood out like whipcord, but it was only harsh laughter which issued forth. 'For God's sake, Tara, is this another of your devious little schemes? You think of everything, don't you? Anything to get me to let you go. Once I'd sampled the pleasures of your eager little body, do you imagine I wouldn't want more? Don't you know you might never get away then?'

The flush in her cheeks deepening to scarlet, Tara stumbled backwards, humiliation making bleak the wide, tormented stare she turned on him. 'That's all you think about, isn't it? The newspapers ... What they might do to your precious Angela?'

There was something frightening about the way his mouth drew in harshly and the words he muttered grimly under his breath. But a moment later he was saying coolly, 'She certainly occupies a great many of my thoughts at present, but not, I would say, as many as you.'

'Naturally it's always the enemy who commands attention.'

'If your weapons were as sharp as your tongue, Miss Curtis, I should have been annihilated long ago.'

Wordlessly Tara turned away, wondering despairingly as she did so how she and this man could be so wonderfully in tune with each other yet, in the next minute, enemies. It hurt painfully to realise he could carry her far beyond the normal bounds of discretion, then instantly reject her. She flushed deeper at what she had so impulsively offered. Never again would she commit such a folly. To fall in love with him had been the worst mistake of the lot but, thank goodness, he need never know about that!

Damon was slanting a wary glance at her, at the tenseness of her face, the unconsciously seductive curves of her figure. 'Are you all right?' he asked.

Her hands clenched. 'Why shouldn't I be?'

'You have no need to be insolent, girl.' His mouth tightened, as if fire still raced along his veins. 'I am not yet so good myself, if it affords you any satisfaction, but

I wouldn't like to offend your sensibilities by putting it any plainer.'

Tara's eyes flickered uncertainly over every taut muscle of his tall figure. She felt like a sleepwalker. Everything he said seemed to draw her unconsciously to him, so she longed to be in his arms. The excitement his voice aroused jerked her breath and her senses, so she was again forced to turn from him. 'What do we do now?' she tried to shrug with supreme indifference.

As if relieved at her easier composure, he sighed. 'We are to return and have lunch on the yacht.'

On the yacht! She didn't want to go there. 'Please, Damon,' she pleaded, her eyes more stricken than she knew, 'don't make me.'

'I'm sure you'll enjoy it.' His voice was clipped as he led her down to the beach.

'No, I don't think so.' Stubbornly she trailed into silence. She wouldn't confess, wild horses wouldn't drag it from her, how it would be torment to retrace old footsteps, relive old memories. Even to catch a glimpse of the yacht an hour ago had been enough to make her quiver.

'We're only visiting her for a meal,' he replied mildly, but as if he wanted to hear no more protests.

'Why have you brought your boat here if you aren't going to use it?' Tara's voice wobbled as she stumbled helplessly on a stone.

'I was going to use it.' His hand steadied her.

'Then ... ?'

'Tara!' he sounded grim, as he waited for her to catch up, 'I refuse to answer a series of questions which you've no right to ask. Maybe one day I will explain, but not now.'

'Which is about as clear as mud,' she retorted defiantly. 'You're a devil, Mr Voulgaris!'

'All the same you'll come and eat on the yacht,' he

said adamantly, his eye glinting. 'As you're so fond of likening me to the devil, Miss Curtis, you might recall how in front of Hades' palace lay the twin pools of Forgetfulness and Memory. On my yacht, this day, you may drink from which one you will. It is entirely up to you, but I want no more fuss!'

Further on, he showed her a narrow wedge cut in the rock which divided the two bays. 'We have no reason to get wet again,' he said, as she stared at the passage in surprise. 'I was already in the water or I would have used it before, when I had to come after you.'

With frustration, Tara realised that they were using this tunnel which at its best could only be described as dank and overgrown, in order to prevent her from again trying to escape. She didn't think she would have a chance, either in or out of the water, with Damon in such close attendance, but he obviously wasn't taking any chances.

When they emerged she was covered with bits of green foliage and knew she must look a mess. 'How can I visit your yacht looking like this?' she asked, this time feeling she had a valid excuse. Angela's swimsuit was torn in two places and streaked with slimy green algae. 'I'll have to replace it,' Tara exclaimed.

'I'm sure she won't expect you to,' he drawled mildly, his eyes pinning Tara's slim figure, so she wished she hadn't drawn his attention. 'She will have many more where that came from.'

'That's not the point, though, is it?' Tara replied, with a resistance she was well aware he found irritating.

His wry sigh expressed it. 'Your own clothes should have arrived at the villa by now. Tim promised to send them when I spoke to him earlier. I left instructions for a servant to bring something casual down to the beach. We are only picnicking on deck.'

Surprisingly neither Angela or Greg appeared to be curious as to where Tara had been as no comments were forthcoming. Angela looked distinctly put out but didn't say anything, so Tara concluded that her chilly face had more to do with Greg than what she and Damon had been doing.

A small boat was waiting to take them out to the yacht and as soon as they were on board Tara asked if she could go and shower. Scarcely pausing for Damon's consenting nod, or to thank him for the package he passed her, she plunged below. On reaching the cabin which she had used before, she sagged against the door, wrapped immediately in bitter-sweet memories.

Then, recalling what Damon had said about the twin pools from Greek mythology, she decided soberly that forgetfulness must be for her. It didn't do, as she had learnt to her cost, to take everything he said too seriously, but in this case, the advice he offered could be wise.

The package which he had given her contained, as he had promised, some of her clothes, and after she showered she dressed quickly, glad to be able to wear her own things again. She was just brushing the tangles from her long fair hair when she heard a knock at the door.

It was Georgios, with a huge mug of steaming hot coffee. 'I thought you might like this,' he smiled. 'Mr Damon told me you'd been swimming and felt cold.'

'Oh, yes. Thank you,' she smiled back uncertainly, while taking the coffee gratefully. 'It was very kind of you to bring it, Georgios.'

After he left, Tara carried her coffee over to the small table. Sitting on the edge of the bed she stared down into the depth of the mug. She had felt cold, but it hadn't been because of the sea. It was simply that Damon Voulgaris didn't love her, and it had come to her suddenly how she'd been a fool ever to think he might. The magnetism between them was probably something he had experienced with a dozen women before her and she would be a stupid little fool to read into it that which didn't exist. Angela Felton was the one who had captured his serious attention. Tara Curtis and her kind were merely playthings!

They had a picnic lunch on deck, as Damon promised, with a setting so perfect it brought tears to Tara's eyes. Aware that Damon had seen them she blinked them away, grateful that after his first narrowed glance he didn't say anything. She couldn't possibly have confessed the exact reason for her unhappiness.

Sighing wistfully, she dropped beside the bulkhead, preferring to be here, where she might stretch her long, bare legs on the warm deck, than on one of the luxurious loungers. Her eyes still damp with longing, she gazed out to sea. How lovely, on a day like this, to have gone sailing with Damon, then come home in the soft dusk to warm log fires and a cosy dinner for two. And afterwards, to share coffee and low, loving murmurings in front of the leaping flames, with no other sound but that of the whispering wind and the distant sigh of the sea.

That was as far as she got before colliding with Damon's eyes and feeling her cheeks grow hot as she suspected he had guessed the line of her thoughts very accurately. For a moment his glance glinted, as if he would like to continue where she left off.

This being too much for even a girl of her foolishness to believe, she stared back at him defiantly. He was sitting beside Angela, who moved every now and again to lay a caressing hand on his arm and press nearer with a bare thigh. Was Greg blind? Tara wondered. Didn't he notice, especially when Damon smoothed Angela's hand before lifting it to press a firm kiss on the back of her long white fingers.

Shivering, Tara recalled how once he had kissed her like that, only then his mouth had touched her palm. Unable to remove her eyes, she was still watching as he lifted his head and looked at her with something which reminded her of impatient regret on his face. Her eyes, cooling contemptuously, jerked away, but not before she noticed a dull red under his tan, an angry tightening of his mouth, betraying anger at her unconcealed opinion of him. Whatever her regard, Tara noticed he didn't exactly shrivel under it. Hollowly she realised he was a man who would bow down before no one, even if they were in the right!

Greg and Angela began an argument about music as they began to eat. Tara, to her surprise, found herself listening with interest as they were served with a delicious hot soup in round pottery bowls. They were naturally very knowledgeable and Tara was astonished to hear herself occasionally daring to join in, and even more surprised to realise she was being listened to. Damon was mostly silent, his eyes never far from Tara's face. He only entered the conversation when it reached an impasse, or to support something Angela said.

After the soup there was fresh lobster salad, with a sparkling white wine, followed by a variety of wonderful cheeses along with rough rye bread and salty butter. Then Georgios brought coffee and brandy and jugs of thick cream. Some picnic, Tara thought wryly, thinking it a meal more fit for a king. The champagne, however, had definitely lightened her mood. So much so that she found herself accepting the glass of brandy Damon placed in her hand without a qualm. She even managed to smile up at him sleepily, as all her worries about everything seemed, momentarily, to disperse.

Angela wanted Greg to go below to listen to one of his recordings, one about which they didn't agree. She invited Damon to go with them but, surprisingly, he declined. This made Angela hesitate, her eyes suddenly suspicious as they darted from him to Tara. But obviously feeling she couldn't change her mind without looking foolish, she followed Greg.

As they disappeared, Damon immediately moved towards Tara. Without warning he dropped down beside her, pulling her roughly against him, crushing her surprised mouth under his own. The wine Tara had drunk seemed to have muddled her head so that somehow she couldn't find the strength to push him away. There seemed nothing she could do to prevent herself falling into a stormy sea of violent desire, with waves of longing washing dizzily through her veins. His mouth was demanding, his hands more so, as he began undoing the buttons of her shirt and slipping it from her shoulders.

With what little breath she appeared to have left, Tara began protesting weakly, but he shushed her hoarsely. His mouth slid down her neck to find the seductive hollow between her breasts, his hands holding her ruthlessly to him. 'If others were not here, Tara Curtis, I would take you to my cabin and seek revenge for certain looks you have been giving me!'

Then suddenly, as Greg and Angela returned, she was free. Tara wasn't sure how long they had been gone, she suspected not long, but she hadn't been aware of anything but each new caressing movement of Damon's fingers.

Then he was away from her and she stumbled clumsily to her feet, muttering something about seeking her things. There was also Angela's swimsuit. She was aching for just a few minutes alone to pull herself together, and her heart sank as she discovered Angela had followed her.

Angela's eyes were cold, but she was clearly furious. 'Just what were you and Damon doing on deck?' she cried, pursuing Tara into the cabin and closing the door. When Tara didn't reply but stared at her in apparent astonishment, she added angrily, 'You were also far too long in that other bay before lunch. I'm not a complete fool, you know!'

'I never thought you were,' Tara whispered, aghast that Angela could get in such a state regarding one man while engaged to another. There was so much here Tara didn't understand, nor did she feel she would ever be able to. 'Perhaps it took Damon a while to catch up with me before lunch,' she said. She had been going on impulsively, to tell Angela that it was she whom Damon really cared

for, but something made her change her mind. Perhaps it
would be no real kindness to try and convince Angela of
this. This way Angela might never make an effort to
straighten out her affairs, but for ever imagine she could
keep two men dangling. Maybe she needed a little push in
another direction.

'When Damon did catch up with me,' Tara forced a
small, secret smile, 'he thought you might enjoy an hour
alone with Greg, and we got on talking ... You know how
it is?' She let her smile grow artlessly.

'You're not trying to tell me Damon would look twice
at a girl like you!' Angela's face went an ugly red with
spite.

Tara giggled carelessly. Rather that than burst into
tears! 'I don't think he's a great believer in just looking,
Miss Felton, not when he has the chance of doing something else!'

Almost choking with anger, Angela hissed, 'I'd advise
you to keep your hands off Damon Voulgaris!'

'Why?' Tara lifted her shoulders in a careless shrug.

'Why!' Angela half screamed, then made an effort to
pull herself together. 'As much for your own good as
anything else. He'd ruin your life because he'd never think
about a girl like you seriously.'

Tara tried not to flinch too obviously, not liking the
way in which Angela rubbed salt in her wounds. 'I don't
know why you're getting so worked up,' she said. 'After
all, it's his brother you're engaged to, not him.'

'I know.' Angela looked around, as if in two minds
about something. Her brow creased, but as her eyes came
back to Tara's fresh young beauty she seemed to come to
a decision. 'That could have been a mistake!' she confided
triumphantly.

Shocked, Tara stared at her, wondering if she had heard
properly. Her own heart was sore and, to her shame, she
had been taunting the other girl, but she hadn't expected

to be taken so seriously. Tara hadn't known Angela for more than a few hours and already she had been made aware of Angela's jealous nature, yet that last sentence shocked her. Surely, in Greg's present state, Angela couldn't be thinking of giving him up!

'I don't understand,' she whispered, stricken. 'You can't be seriously contemplating ending your engagement?'

'Why not?' Angela was openly insolent now. 'Damon is in love with me, and he's a millionaire. Greg might be devastated, but he'll recover. I'm sure Damon would adore me to be married in white and even his worst enemy couldn't deny he would make the most handsome bridegroom. Can you imagine it, Miss Curtis, how I'll come floating up the aisle and he'll turn and just stare at me?'

Feeling slightly sick, Tara whispered feebly, 'But how long have you known him?'

Angela still rode on a wave of elation. 'Longer than you, my girl!' Then suddenly she paused. 'My God! Am I a fool! You're a journalist! You probably intend publishing every word I'm saying!'

Instantly Tara felt suspicious of Angela's exaggerated dismay. 'Even if I were what you think I am, I'm scarcely in a position to get any sort of story published at the moment,' she said tersely.

Angela paused suggestively. 'But it would be quite a story, when you are! It might be a long time before the gossip columns will have anything more exciting. Greek millionaire marries the girl he has always been secretly in love with.'

'Always?' Tara whispered hollowly.

Angela's face was the epitome of sharp smugness as she nodded, although she didn't enlarge on it. 'I take it Damon doesn't intend keeping you here permanently.'

'I'm afraid I don't follow?' Tara tried to hide a sudden apprehension at something unmistakably frightening in Angela's voice.

Angela shrugged. 'Then you must be blind as well as

stupid. Can't you see that he won't let you go until you're in no position to say anything against either him or his guests!'

Hurt stabbed through Tara like a thousand daggers and she went white. So this was what Damon had been leading up to? What a fool she had been not to have guessed! On deck, when he had kissed her, she had noticed, when she had been able to pull herself sufficiently together to notice anything at all, how there had been a smouldering anger behind his grey eyes. Anger he hadn't been able to control, caused by the continuing necessity of having to keep her here. She had put it down, in her folly, to emotional impatience. Now she could scarcely believe her own stupidity. It was almost as ridiculous and crazy as this whole situation and she must have been out of her mind to think that Damon was beginning to care. It had been incredibly foolish to fall in love with him, but, just as long as he had no inkling of this, it might at least be possible to salvage some of her pride.

Tara closed her eyes to hide the pain they might betray and momentarily gathered a little strength. Of course, wasn't what Angela had suggested just a bit absurd? If Damon had wanted to ruin her reputation to the extent Angela was suggesting, couldn't he have done it last night? Yet who, Tara wondered, with a suddenly sinking heart, would believe he had left her entirely innocent? He might even have servants ready to vouch that they had spent the night together. That he would never need such evidence to blackmail her into silence was something he obviously didn't believe, and it hurt more than anything to know he wouldn't think twice of using it against her.

CHAPTER TEN

HER face pale but composed, Tara looked at Angela steadily. 'I'm sure there's no truth in your allegations, and I believe you know it. Damon might try to frighten me, but I scarcely think he would be such a fool as to go as far as you imply. Not,' she faltered bitterly, 'under the very nose of the girl he would obviously like to have for his wife—if she didn't happen to be engaged to his brother!'

The rest of the warm afternoon passed, but was so heavy with inexplicable undercurrents that even Angela's brittle, sophisticated gaiety seemed dampened. Afterwards Greg spoke of being aware of a certain atmosphere, of feeling it a bad omen, but to Tara those strange, sunlit hours only seemed to reflect the dark image of her own unhappiness.

Damon, after showing a mocking consideration Tara coldly rejected, transferred his attention to Angela again. Showing her some photographs which he had taken in Bangkok, when he had visited Thailand, he sat with a casual hand on her shoulder while suggesting it might be a good place to spend a honeymoon. On the other hand the Bahamas had just about everything and Nassau was fun. Tara hated the eagerly enquiring expression on Angela's face as she glanced up at him, meeting the blandness of his sardonic smile. A honeymoon with Damon Voulgaris! Tara shivered slightly, encountering his narrowed eyes accidentally, not wishing to dwell on the heart-stopping relevance of that!

Turning quickly away, she glanced at Greg. To her surprise he was taking little notice of the intimacy which appeared to exist between Damon and his fiancée. Didn't he mind? she wondered in amazement, not for the first time. He seemed sunk in a continuing depression and she won-

168

dered anxiously if Damon didn't realise what he was doing. In flirting so blatantly with Angela, wasn't he frightened of pushing Greg too far?

When Damon decided it was time to return to the villa, Tara made little effort to hide her relief. Nothing could be worse than having to sit enduring the torture of his intimate conversation with Angela and the cool, calculating glances he frequently slanted in her own direction.

After the small boat returned them to the shore they made their way silently back up the cliff. Angela went first with Damon, but somehow they became separated and Tara found him by her side, with the other two in front. In a self-confessed hurry to have a leisurely bath before dinner, Angela hurried on, obviously not noticing that Damon had left her.

'Don't you feel the same feminine urge?' Damon mocked, so close behind Tara on the last bit of the steep incline that she could actually feel his breath in her hair and the long length of his powerful thigh touching hers.

Flinching, she stumbled and, losing her balance, half fell back against him. His hand caught her waist and it seemed to Tara that before setting her firmly on her feet he pulled her closer, in a savage desire to hurt. For a brief instant, on contact with what seemed almost every inch of his hard muscled body, the breath was driven from her, so he had to ask his question again. This time the mockery was unmistakable.

'Don't you wish to go and make yourself beautiful for me?'

'No!'

'How emphatic you can sound. Perhaps you ought to take a few lessons in the art of pleasing a man from Angela?'

'Perhaps,' Tara hated his sarcasm. 'But I couldn't ever hope to be as good as Miss Felton!'

'At least she showed some interest in honeymoons,' he said suavely, 'which was more than you did.'

'Perhaps if it were mine under discussion, I might, too,' Tara muttered, badly driven.

'Ah,' he paused, his eyes glinting devilishly, 'so you do know what honeymoons are for? When you get that far,' he added, unrelentingly, his eyes sliding to the lovely curve of her breast, 'you won't be able to run away.'

Feeling flustered and angry, she exclaimed, 'If I ever get that far it certainly won't be with a man like you!'

'Don't be too sure, you little devil.' Catching hold of her arm he held her easily, his steely fingers not allowing her to escape while he tormented her. 'You need a man like me who is able to manage you. Once I had you alone and in my arms you would soon lose any desire to further your regrettable career.'

'Why, you——!' Momentarily at loss for words, Tara glared up at him while colour flooded her pale cheeks. There was no sign of either Angela or Greg and her whole body began trembling as, from the diabolical expression in Damon's eyes, she had the terrifying conviction that he was about to prove his point. And, as she swayed helplessly towards him, she knew she couldn't do a thing to stop him.

Then suddenly they were interrupted as a servant came hurrying from the house. There was a message. It had just arrived. Damon was wanted urgently.

With a curt word of excuse Damon left her to follow the man indoors. More slowly Tara walked after them. Damon's business contacts seemed to pursue him endlessly. Even the few days she had spent with him on board his yacht had seldom been free from such interruptions.

On reaching the hall she was surprised to find Angela there with Greg. She had expected they would be upstairs. Greg was standing with his hands pushed into his pockets looking bored, while Angela frowned uncertainly and turned to Tara, as if driven by a need to speak to someone who might take notice of her.

'There's an urgent message from London. Damon thinks it could be my father.'

Greg shrugged, walking stairwards. 'Well, I'm not waiting to hear. He will only be wanting to know when you're going home.'

'That wouldn't be urgent,' Angela pointed out sharply and not, Tara thought, unreasonably. 'I've noticed you don't seem overwhelmingly interested in your future father-in-law!'

'Sorry, darling.' Greg's mouth twisted as he lifted careless eyebrows. 'The fact is I have little in common with my future daddy-in-law! I don't like him, but then you'd be foolish to pretend the feeling isn't mutual.'

'That's a beastly thing to say, but perhaps you're right.' Angela paused, her eyes hard. 'In fact I'm beginning to wonder ...' She broke off as Damon came out of the study. 'Oh, darling,' she cried, starting towards him, her long white hands thrown out appealingly, 'was it Daddy? What does he want?'

Damon, Tara noticed, was pale, but his mouth was firm, as though he saw no sense in prevarication. As Angela reached him his arm went gently around her. 'It was about your father,' he said carefully, his eyes compassionate. 'I'm afraid he died this afternoon. There's no easy way of breaking such news. I'm extremely sorry, Angela.'

Tara stood very still although her pulse was racing. In that moment there was something about Damon Voulgaris which commanded respect. If about him there had been a brief hesitation, he had known there was little he could really do to soften such a blow. Not for the first time she was conscious of his superior years, the additional wisdom they must bring. She was a lot younger than Damon and, while this was not something she could change, perhaps it was up to her to prove she could act with dignity, show the same restrained sympathy, when necessary.

'Miss Felton—Angela,' she began, going to the other

girl at once, laying a warm hand on her shoulder, 'I'm very sorry.'

It came as a shock to find her hand tartly brushed aside, as Angela's eyes sharpened with quick anger. 'You're a stranger, Miss Curtis. I don't require any sympathy from you.'

'Angela!' Strangely enough it was Greg's exclamation of disapproving surprise which broke the startled silence.

Tara frowned at the hardness of his voice, shaking her head slightly, trying to tell him it didn't matter, that Angela would be too shocked to know what she was saying.

The silence continued for several seconds. Damon left them and came back with a drink for Angela, for which she thanked him. Taking a sip, she spoke in a low voice to her fiancé. 'Greg, I'd like to speak to you for a few minutes.'

As they disappeared into the lounge, Tara stared down at the tiles on the floor, not knowing what else to do. She hadn't ever known Angela's father, but she had the crazy impression she was more stunned than his daughter at the news of his sudden death.

Damon stayed with her but didn't come near her, nor did he speak. He looked so coldly distant he was like someone she had never known. Nervousness prompted her to say anxiously, 'I was only trying to help.'

'Of course.'

She glanced at him again, her fingers clenching slowly. He sounded oddly detached, deep in thought yet with a kind of taut expectancy about him. Naturally he would be thinking of Angela's grief—even if she had a strange way of showing it. Whatever his private views regarding Angela's reactions, he wouldn't condemn her. Clearly his concern for her absorbed him. He must be considering her sorrow, when full realisation eventually hit her, all the problems she would have to face on her return to England. No doubt he would be returning with her as Greg, owing to the state of his nerves, wouldn't be able to give her much practical assistance. Tara, in that moment, especially as Damon ignored her, felt utterly a stranger, completely shut out.

Only a short time elapsed before Angela and Greg re-appeared. Tara felt, with a slightly hysterical sense of unreality, it was rather like a game of charades. Unfortunately Angela's stark announcement, as she reached them, shocked away any fleeting frivolity.

Angela paused, rather like an actress coming on stage, her face pale but her composure unimpaired. She had the enviable air of someone who knows exactly what they are doing. Stopping beside Damon again, she laid a tentative hand on his arm, her eyes softly appealing. 'Greg and I have broken our engagement. I'm convinced it was a mistake and Greg has released me.'

There was dead silence. Greg said nothing. He just sat down, as though nothing much had happened. Tara's eyes fixed on Damon's with agonising futility. What she had thought to find in his dark features she wasn't sure, but she could read nothing from his sardonic grimness, as his glance left his brother swiftly to return to Angela. Tara noticed, sickly, how the hand Angela rested on his arm was bereft of an engagement ring.

Angela went on quickly, as if she realised there was some need to justify such an action at a time like this. 'I know,' she said, a pathetic huskiness in her voice, 'you're all wondering how I could bring myself to break my engagement immediately after hearing about Daddy, but his death will cause enough speculation. Feeling the way I do about Greg, I think it would be wrong to drag him with me through all the ensuing publicity. I don't love him, and he agrees with me that someone else could be better to help me through the next few days.'

She was looking directly at Damon as she spoke and Tara felt suddenly ill. Angela was quite obviously laying her cards on the table, and it seemed to Tara she was using her father's death to further her own ends, without any real feeling of sorrow. Tara felt stunned that anyone could think of themselves to such an extent, in the face of such a tragic event. When her own father had been so ill, even the thought of losing him had made her feel terribly sad.

Feeling suffocated with scorn, she saw how Angela continued to gaze up at Damon, yet this was nothing to the despair which attacked her when she heard Angela pleading, 'Damon darling, would you come home with me? I need someone.'

'Naturally,' Damon replied softly, picking up Angela's hand and transferring it expressionlessly to his lips. Almost, Tara reflected fiercely, as if this was the signal he had been waiting for. There was to be no more of his former hesitation, which had allowed another man to whisk away the woman he loved. Hadn't he once said, 'I knew her first?' Quickly he said, ignoring both Tara and Greg, 'You will wish to leave immediately. I'll arrange for us to be picked up as soon as possible. With any luck we could be away within the hour.'

'I'll go and pack a few things.' Angela gave him a wan smile, only her eyes betraying a sudden excitement as he released her hand. 'You can arrange to have what I leave sent on as I don't suppose we'll be back here for a long time. Islands like Polos don't really suit me anyway, darling. Much too quiet.'

'Of course.'

Tara stared at him, not attempting to hide her strangled horror at the way in which he appeared willing to grovel. He was certainly losing no time in letting Angela know he was ready to indulge her every wish, to obey her every command! She had heard that love could change a man, but she had never dreamt ever to see Damon Voulgaris humbling himself like this. Her face white with the force of her feeling, Tara turned away, but not before Damon caught a glimpse of the contempt in her eyes.

About to stride into his study to make the necessary arrangements, he paused to stare at her, his face viciously angry. 'Before I go, Tara, I'll take you back to the taverna.'

'Surely her brother would come ...' Angela began coldly.

'No!' Damon rapped adamantly. 'I don't want anyone else here, my dear. I'll take her myself and be rid of her. I don't think she can harm any of us now.'

Tara was waiting, once again, with her shabby case, when Damon returned, saying all was arranged. Angela had gone to her room without wishing Tara goodbye. Tara hadn't really expected it and, though she had tried, she hadn't been able to say goodbye herself. She just hoped she would never see Angela again.

Now Tara went out with Damon to his car. He took no notice of her renewed plea to be allowed to walk and left her with no alternative but to climb in to his luxurious limousine.

'I will see you delivered personally,' he grated, his jaw tightening as he intercepted her loathing glance. 'And you can take that look off your face or I'll give you something to really justify its existence!'

As his tires ripped savagely, she jeered, 'You forget you have no time to do anything to me now!'

'What I have in mind wouldn't take all that long,' he muttered savagely. 'I should have made you mine long ago. It would have subdued you. You would no longer be questioning my actions!'

Her breath caught but strangely her fury abated, tears suddenly dampening her cheeks.

Perhaps he caught the glitter of them, for he exclaimed harshly, 'Tara, I have to talk to you, and all you do is arouse my anger!'

Wildly she broke in, doubting if she could stand any more, 'I don't want to listen. Anyway, I think I've heard just about the lot. No wonder you didn't want the press around! I—I just don't understand you ...'

'Perhaps you've never tried very hard.' His voice was curt.

Flicking him a tortured glance, she saw the lines of strain around his mouth. All for a woman like Angela Felton, she thought hopelessly. 'I could never understand a man who did everything possible to steal his brother's fiancée, especially when he's supposed to be helping him! Are congratulations in order, now that you've succeeded?'

'Damn you!' There was no mistaking the underlying violence.

Tara willed herself to stop shaking. 'If it hadn't been so—so premeditated! You haven't even the excuse that it just happened. You must have known, with Greg here, Angela would follow.'

'You will be quiet!' This as they reached the taverna and he slammed on the brakes. He turned on her savagely, his hand clenched the steering wheel, his knuckles white, his face so barbarous she felt frightened. 'I refuse to listen any longer to your insults! If you were a man I would kill you for what I think you are trying to say. For what is obviously your opinion of me. If I had more time I would indeed carry you to some lonely spot and make you regret each and every word you have uttered!'

Tara knew her face had gone as cold as ice because the tears which began streaming down it scalded her skin. The way he spoke shocked her dreadfully, but not so much as the way he looked. His hard, handsome face seemed to glitter with fury and she could quite believe he would have liked to have strangled her with his bare hands. He would have enjoyed doing it, too, and what hope would she have had of surviving the brutal strength of his merciless body? With such rage driving him he might have crushed her more easily than he might a fly!

Temper was the only means of protection she could think of, the only weapon to effectively disguise the true state of her feelings. She glared at him defiantly, her cheeks still wet. 'I won't apologise, so it's no use waiting. I see no reason why I should, anyway, and you can threaten all you like. You're nothing but a cheat and a coward, Damon Voulgaris, and I think it's high time someone had the courage to tell you so!'

His hand lifted and he slapped her hard, so there was a terrible ringing in her ears. Her cheek stung and she heard herself gasp as the eyes she drowned in looked colder than Arctic seas. There was a hot red mark on her face, a frozen ring around her heart, and she felt terrible. In another minute she was sure, if she didn't get away from him, she would be ill.

Her hand groped for the door. 'Goodbye, Mr Voulgaris!'

'Not so fast,' he stopped her harshly but with no apparent pity for her obviously shaken state. 'I will see your brother.'

He was a remote stranger and she didn't care how she looked. She was sobbing silently now, but with rising hysteria. As he leant over her to prevent her leaving, she cried wildly against the hard weight of him. 'They might not want me back, so you'd better spare yourself any possible embarrassment. I could be following you and your lady love back to London.'

The curse under his breath was quite audible to her sensitive ears. When he turned his head his face was only inches from her own. 'I won't tell you again to be quiet. Are you ever going to do as you're told?'

'Yes,' she whispered, cowardly, because so near, she went strangely weak, unable any longer to defy him. The sick feeling in her stomach grew worse and she recalled stupidly how he had once laid his hand there. How it had stilled, for one breathless moment, all desire to escape him. Inside her, now, she felt the same nameless ache, the same longing. It was like chasing over hazy rainbows in a crazy attempt to locate an as yet unknown delight.

The anger still in the man who loomed over her kept his voice rough. 'I was hoping we would be able to talk rationally, but I'm afraid it's too late. I want you to go straight to your room while I speak to Tim. You will remain there.'

'No!'

His hands were immediately on her neck and she realised he might easily strangle her. Then he paused and, just as her body tensed in terror, she felt him touching her face, correctly assessing the pain and anguish within her. As her breath caught, his hands slipped to her narrow waist, gripping tightly before spanning upwards. Her breath quickened against the sudden rasp of his as a frightening rapture flooded her, and, involuntarily, she turned up her face, her lips parting.

'Now will you do as I ask?' He didn't pretend not to be fully aware of the hold he had over her as he narrowly studied the hectic flush on her cheeks but ignored the wanton invitation of her mouth. There was just the slight shake of his hand, as he impatiently thrust back the rumpled hair from off his broad forehead, to indicate how sorely he was tempted.

'Yes.' The fight went completely out of her as she slumped bleakly, realising how he was using her to get his own way. Yet no longer could she find the strength to struggle against him. Unhappiness came over her in huge waves, drowning her, as her face fell.

'Come then, it grows late.' Again he said something half under his breath. This time, although she couldn't make it out, she felt there was more than a hint of regret. His eyes studied the trembling betrayal of her mouth, his own hardening with cruel resolution. 'Too much is at stake to take foolish risks.'

Quickly he released her and, as if in a dream, Tara allowed him to help her from the car into the taverna. Then she was in her room, scarcely knowing how she'd got there, and a short while afterwards not even the sound of Damon leaving was enough to break the terrible drugged feeling of numbness which seemed to encompass her. When

Veronica came to ask if she would like to join them for dinner, she merely smiled and shook her head.

The next morning, however, she managed to get down to breakfast as if nothing had happened. She even managed to ask casually if Damon had been able to find Tim the previous evening. When he nodded, she asked what it was that Damon had wanted to speak to him about.

Shooting her a quick glance, Tim replied evasively that Damon had simply wished to explain a few things, and that they'd all probably be better to forget what had happened since Tara had come to the island, and begin again.

Veronica, pouring Tara coffee, and being more friendly that Tara ever remembered, added her pleas to Tim's, so that Tara found it difficult to be ungracious.

'Often the past is better forgotten,' she agreed dismally, 'but I think it would be better if I went straight home.' She had no wish to face the misery of remaining on Polos, where every inch seemed permeated with Damon's strong personality, even when he was away.

But they wouldn't hear of her going and eventually extracted a promise that she would stay for at least another two weeks.

'The Frenchman has gone,' Tim explained, 'and I'd like to take Veronica for a short holiday. She hasn't been feeling herself lately, and I believe this is what she needs.'

This, Tara realised, must be his way of apologising for Veronica's behaviour at the villa, and Tara liked the way he managed to do it without apparently criticising his wife. 'Where were you thinking of going?' She gave him a warmer smile.

'Athens,' Tim answered briefly. 'I'll arrange for someone to be here with you while we're away. All you have to do is keep an eye on everything.'

It would have been churlish to refuse, especially as Veronica's face began to glow in anticipation of the first real holiday she and Tim had had in years. 'Have you fixed up some place to stay?' Tara tried to show some proper interest.

'I—we——' for a moment Tim appeared strangely confused. 'Oh, yes. That is . . .'

'A friend has loaned us his flat,' Veronica put in quickly, bestowing on Tim a sharp glance.

Tara saw it, but she was already wondering about something else. 'What about the boatyard? While you're away, I mean?' She added the last sentence hurriedly, to cover up. She had no wish to disturb the new harmony which seemed to exist, but surely it was only days ago since Tim had told her how the work in the boatyard was so far behind it might have to close down?

'It won't come to any harm until we get back,' Tim shrugged, utterly surprising her.

The couple who came to keep her company while they were gone startled Tara even more. The man was well dressed and strong and very intelligent. He looked as though he could be at the height of some chosen career which had involved considerable training. His wife was extremely pleasant and told Tara she occasionally did secretarial work in Athens where, Tara presumed curiously, Tim and Veronica must have met them. Tim and Veronica, however, had left almost as soon as the others had arrived, so Tara had learnt very little. Her watchdogs, as she tended secretly to call them, would tell her nothing either and, rather than suffer from a vexed sense of frustration, she stopped trying to pry.

Jonathan rang. He told Tara, rather belatedly she thought, to forget about the Greg Golden affair. He appeared to know everything about Greg's broken engagement and that he was back in England.

'His fiancée, or ex-fiancée, rather, apparently has her sights on bigger fish.'

Tara rang off with a muttered excuse, knowing only too well whom Jonathan was referring to but unable to stay and listen to him actually putting a name to the——

bigger fish! It would soon be common knowledge that Damon Voulgaris, the Greek millionaire, was the enduring love of Miss Felton's life. Probably, as soon as was decently possible after her father's funeral, Angela's new engagement would be announced.

Wondering how much more pain she must suffer, Tara stared out through the kitchen window to where the waves were breaking gently on the shore. Yet Damon had never promised her anything, so, no matter how dreadful the torture, she had no valid reason to complain.

Fretting so much to be away from the island, it didn't help when Tim contacted her to say that he and Veronica would like to stay in Athens a few more days. There was a boat business on the mainland which attracted him.

'I was hoping you wouldn't be much longer,' Tara found herself protesting, but in the end she allowed herself to be talked into staying, at least until the end of the week.

'You sound rather tearful,' Tim pondered, then startled and angered her by asking smoothly, 'You wouldn't be fretting for Damon Voulgaris?'

As with Jonathan, she abruptly rang off, wondering furiously how she ever came to have two such brothers. Yet Tim's absence did give her a sense of security, even while she grew anxious about it. There must be no chance of Damon returning or Tim would certainly have been back. Hadn't Damon threatened to close him down if he didn't work harder—or words to that effect? No, Tim would never risk Damon coming here and finding him on holiday in Athens, and neglecting his business.

As the weekend drew nearer and so, it seemed, her impending departure, Tara gave in to a sudden impulse to walk along the shore, to see if Damon's yacht still lay in the bay below his villa. She hadn't felt able to ask any of the villagers who might have known, for she found it impossible to mention Damon at all, so there was only one way she could find out. After tea she put on a pair of faded old shorts and a thin shirt and set off. Thinking it wise, she did tell her two companions where she was going, but to her relief neither objected or tried to follow, which proved a relief. Tim might imagine he was showing a proper sense of responsibility, having her so well looked after, but it grew irksome at times, and did seem he was being over-protective on an island the size of Polos.

Walking quickly in the cool of the late afternoon, it didn't take Tara very long to reach the villa, but as she breasted the cliff top she saw the white yacht was gone and the bay lay empty. Almost, she thought wearily, as empty as her heart, her entire life, now that Damon was gone.

'Tara!'

At first she was convinced his voice was just an echo of her thoughts, or from the times she had woken during the long nights, imagining he was bending over her, her name on his lips. Stricken with unhappiness, she refused to look around, not until she heard him speak again, this time too clearly for her to go on believing she was just dreaming. There was something in his voice, too. A kind of deep passion which surely never belonged to a ghost.

'Damon?' He was right behind her and she felt herself sway, but his hand went out to catch her as she stumbled. Shock ran through her, dissolving into wild panic. What was Damon doing here? Desperately she tried to calm the frightened race of her heart which seemed to be shaking her whole body. Her eyes widened, her glance flickered nervously past his shoulder, expecting to see Angela Felton.

'Are you looking for someone?' He still held her arm while his eyes searched her white face.

Tara flushed, trying not to look at him. 'I thought perhaps Miss Felton . . .'

'She isn't with me.'

Of course it would be too soon after Angela's bereavement. Remembering the way she had parted from him, Tara bit her lip uncertainly. Angela wasn't here, but he wouldn't have come back just to finish that argument! 'I'm sorry,' she said, without meaning to, 'for losing my temper.'

'If you're referring to our last infamous parting, then you can forget it. There won't be another.'

Tara didn't like the sound of that. Nor could she understand why he should be staring at her so intently. She was sure her old blue shorts and red shirt were too shabby to warrant such attention. Too late she recalled that he wouldn't know Tim was away and she hadn't had a chance to warn them he was back.

'Are you staying long?' She felt torn between the misery of knowing this would be the last time she would see him and hope that he would soon be gone, for Tim's sake. 'Maybe,' she mumbled, when Damon's strange silence continued, 'Maybe you've just come to collect something?'

'I have.'

'I see.'

'You're thinner.' He appeared to concentrate on her closely, his hand going out to brush back her long fair hair. 'Your face ...' he frowned. 'Is it possible, in so short a time?'

'Damon!'

'Yes?' His voice was suddenly taut.

'I must get back. I'm sorry.' She knew she couldn't stay with him much longer without breaking down. 'They'll be wondering where I've got to, at the taverna.'

'Don't worry, Cosmos knows you are with me.'

The green of Tara eyes deepened with astonishment. 'You know him?'

'I should, he works for me.'

'Works for you?' Tara shook her head helplessly. 'I think I must be going crazy!'

'I hope so!' Suddenly, like steel, his arms went around her, as he drew her to him. 'At least I want you crazy about me! If not, then you'll have to decide you're going to be, my darling, because from now on I'm never going to let you go.'

Her heart thudding with a mixture of stunned surprise and enchantment, Tara lifted her thick lashes to gaze at him. At the back of his dark eyes she saw desire and a smouldering passion, but there was also a depth of tenderness she had never been allowed a glimpse of before. Yet all the pain she had suffered forced a bewildered caution. 'I don't understand?' Aghast she whispered, hoarsely, 'There's a lot of things I don't understand. Angela, for instance?'

'I realise.' Looking as though he would rather have crushed her to him than waste time on words, he exclaimed savagely, 'Do you not imagine I have wanted to explain? I even felt you had some explaining to do yourself, my child, but I was in no position to take what would obviously have been the only sensible course—to get you alone and have it out with you!'

'But you mistrusted me!' Tara's eyes suddenly glittered with tears, as she lifted her head from his broad chest.

'In a way,' he sighed, 'yes. The evidence did weigh rather heavily against you, but usually I don't worry too much about the press. It was really Angela and Greg, there was so much at stake. Anyway, since I left I've seen your brother Jonathan, who has confessed he used what amounted almost to blackmail. I have also seen your parents, my darling, and, if it makes you any happier, I left them all well content.'

Tara's face paled. Damon seemed to be telling her something, but she found it difficult to believe he really cared. Perhaps she'd be wiser not to take the endearments he uttered too seriously. 'What about Angela?' she persisted. 'When you left, Damon, I thought you loved Angela?'

'This is what I have to explain. It is not Angela I care about but you. But, my child,' he pressed a brief kiss full of tender violence on her softly parted mouth, 'before we go into this there is a lot you must understand.' Not listening to her dazed protests, he pulled her gently down on to a soft sward of grass, his arms still around her. 'It was all arranged before I met you, otherwise it would never have happened.'

'What wouldn't?' Tara, feeling the hard warmth of him through the thinness of her shirt, stilled an involuntary shudder. Suddenly she seemed to lose interest in everything but the need to cling to him and had to make herself listen. 'What wouldn't?' she repeated numbly, as he paused, as though sharing the same inclinations himself.

'My involvement with Greg and Angela,' he sighed. 'You see, it was through me that Greg met Angela. I would have given anything to have avoided such a meeting, as she is not a woman I admire. I don't like saying it about any woman, but for years she has been pursuing me, although I have never given her the least encouragement. One evening she found me in my London flat and we were in the middle of a rather bitter row when Greg walked in. The bitterness was on her side, it was contempt on mine. Angela saw Greg as a means of avenging herself on me. I couldn't be sure of this, of course, and was forced to accept their engagement. I had very grave doubts, but Greg was old enough and, I presumed, well able to look after himself, considering the way he lived.

'Subsequent events, however, proved the engagement a mistake. She went off with other men but, at the same time, refused to release Greg. This was when he broke down and begged for my help. I didn't want to be involved but felt I couldn't refuse. Our mother, I'm afraid, is not at all maternal, and to look after Greg has become a habit and, like all habits, difficult to break. He came to Polos and Angela followed, when she heard I was to be there. Greg was sure it was me she still wanted and I decided if this was really true she was no good to Greg. This was why I didn't want the press around. I just hoped everything would fade out quietly.'

'That was why you were so furious at me? When you thought ...'

Damon stopped her with a wry kiss. 'You were why I regretted the whole affair before it even got started.' His arms tightened roughly. 'Heaven help me, but I'd never been in love before. Attraction I had known, but nothing deeper. It wasn't until I saw a girl standing on the sea-front at Piraeus that this soul-shaking experience happened to me.'

Tara stared at him, her pulse racing, her cheeks suddenly ashen from the strength of her emotions. 'You can't mean —me?'

'Indeed I do,' his voice was thick. 'I've been almost out of my mind, you uncaring little brat!' A rueful smile belying the severity of his words, he continued, 'When I discovered, or thought I'd discovered, what you were, I believed you'd only pretended to respond to me in order to get news. You won't ever know what I felt like doing to you!'

'But I changed my mind about helping Jonathan.' While she only wanted to dwell on the wonder of his love, Tara knew an urgent desire to get her side of things straightened out too. 'I never wanted to do what he asked me, but you would never let me explain. You don't know how terrible it felt to have you so furious with me.'

'Maybe I did believe you,' his mouth trailed her cheek, the tear that fell softly, 'but I couldn't let Greg down and this meant taking no risks. If Angela had received even a hint of suspicion that we were attracted to each other I don't think she would ever have broken her engagement. And, with this in mind, I wasn't sure what Greg would do. I felt if he did something stupid I would be responsible. This was why, when it all worked out more or less as I'd expected, I had to get Angela back to London. I felt badly about her father's death, although it had nothing to do with me, but I felt compelled to see her safely home, before leaving her.'

'You could have told me . . .'

'I was going to tell you, at least a little, when I took you back to the taverna, but all we did was quarrel and my Greek temper was too strong. I wanted to kiss you, to tell you how much I loved you, but pride got in the way and I wanted to punish you instead, for the things you said to me.'

Tara was dazed. 'But you saw Tim and Veronica ...?'

'Yes,' without shame he watched her bewilderment, 'I arranged that they should go to Athens, so you should be more or less forced to stay here. I told them we were to be married, although you didn't yet know it. I also arranged for Cosmos and his wife to come and look after you, while we were gone. He is on my security staff and experienced, but I warned him his life would be forfeit should anything happen to you before I got back.'

'Oh, Damon ...' If there seemed nothing else she could think of to say, he didn't appear to notice as he caught her suddenly closer, so that her body moulded to the warmth and hardness of his. His mouth descended, crushing the trembling softness of hers, his kiss hardening and lengthening into passion.

When he released her she groaned, her head whirling as she turned it against the hard maleness of his broad chest.

He allowed her this much reprieve but little more. 'We will be married, my darling, straight away. Maybe I should give you more time, but I find I can't. I did intend you should know me better.' He paused, staring down at her softly flushed face. 'Do you remember how I tried to detain you for a few days on the yacht, under the pretext of having to visit friends?' As Tara nodded in confusion, he added, 'Then Greg got in touch to say Angela had already arrived. He begged me to come to Polos quickly and, while I agreed, I'd never felt so frustrated and angry in my life. It was no help either,' he cast her a grimly reproachful glance, 'that everything between us seemed to be going wrong.'

'It was because I loved you,' Tara confessed weakly, feeling her bones melt to water at his words. 'At least I realised I was beginning to care. Damon,' she suddenly frowned anxiously, 'are you sure Angela will be all right?'

'Forget her, Tara,' he said dryly. 'She was always one to cut her losses. When I left she was almost in the arms of a distant cousin, who I believe shares the estate.'

'I see,' Tara sighed, her brow still creased, as she found something else to worry her even more. 'You're so wealthy, Damon, how can I marry you?'

'You're going to, darling, so don't argue.' With a teasing smile he kissed her flushed cheek. 'In the weeks, the years to come, I intend having some revenge for the way you've made me suffer. There will be no more escaping through the night, no more driving me half mad with frustration! Greg is going to have proper treatment and will soon be himself again. Tim and Veronica will have a new business near Athens. There will be no one you can run to for help during the long months we will spend here on Polos. I'm going to adore you for the rest of your life,' his eyes smouldered with a passionate tenderness. 'I'm going to love you until you scream for mercy, and then I'm not sure I will grant you any.'

Tara trembled as she clung to him. His eyes were wholly threatening, but his mouth was strangely gentle, completely in tune, it seemed, with the urgent happiness rising wildly inside her. 'I'm not sure that I'll want any— mercy from you. I love you too much,' she whispered, drawing his head down, no longer trying to hide the eager desire within her. As their lips met and his arms held her tightly, the peace and silence of the island enfolded them, and Tara knew it would be for ever.

4 FREE
Harlequin Romances

Get all the latest books before they're sold out!

As a Harlequin subscriber you actually receive your personal copies of the latest Romances immediately after they come off the press, so you're sure of getting all 6 each month.

Cancel your subscription whenever you wish!

You don't have to buy any minimum number of books. Whenever you decide to stop your subscription just let us know and we'll cancel all further shipments.

Your FREE gift includes

- **Anne Hampson** — Beyond the Sweet Waters
- **Anne Mather** — The Arrogant Duke
- **Violet Winspear** — Cap Flamingo
- **Nerina Hilliard** — Teachers Must Learn

FREE GIFT CERTIFICATE

and Subscription Reservation

Mail this coupon today!

In U.S.A.:
Harlequin Reader Service
MPO Box 707
Niagara Falls, NY 14302

In Canada:
Harlequin Reader Service
649 Ontario Street
Stratford, Ontario
N5A 6W4

Harlequin Reader Service:

Please send me my 4 Harlequin Romance novels
FREE. Also, reserve a subscription to the 6 NEW
Harlequin Romance novels published each month.
Each month I will receive 6 NEW Romance novels at
the low price of $1.25 each (Total — $7.50 a month).
There are no shipping and handling or any other
hidden charges. I may cancel this arrangement at any
time, but even if I do, these first 4 books are still mine
to keep.

NAME _____ (PLEASE PRINT)

ADDRESS _____

CITY   STATE/PROV.   ZIP/POSTAL CODE

Offer not valid to present subscribers
Offer expires February 28, 1981

R2350

Prices subject to change without notice.